OZZIE

THE STORY OF A YOUNG HORSE

Elaine Heney

For further information, please visit:

www.irishhorsemanship.com

Thank you to Ozzie, John, Margaret,

Pia and Cecile.

Other books by Elaine Heney:

The Little Book of Good Horsemanship

Gentle Horsemanship for Young Riders CDROM

For more information please visit:

www.irishhorsemanship.com

Table of contents

01. The sales

'Lot 24: Grey geld. five yrs. About 14.3h. Broken and riding.'

The black and white catalogue entry was brief and basic, buried amongst two hundred similar entries. Not that we had paid much attention to it yet.

Dad and I had left earlier that morning from Tipperary and we had arrived in Kilkenny just after 12.30pm. I would often come to the sales when I was younger, tagging along after Dad. We spent days looking at horses of all makes and models. Some were well trained and confident and some green as the grass they ate. Some weren't too pretty, some looked great on paper and the lucky ones also looked good in person. I was never too picky. If it had four legs and a tail, looked like a horse and smelled like a horse it was good enough for me. We would walk around all two hundred stables, peering into the darkness to see what each contained. I usually had my own opinions on the various horses we saw.

'Dad, I really like the nervous bay one. He's pretty skinny and I kinda feel sorry for him....'

I was usually correct, but luckily Dad was more discerning. He had a natural eye for a horse. When he found a big scopey horse he liked, that horse was usually pretty special. They were often amongst the best trained jumping horses out with the Scarteens.

'I see what you mean,' Dad would reply, 'but he's back at the knee and his back legs are a bit hooky. We'll have to keep looking. What do you think of this chestnut?'

And so we'd march on, assessing every horse we met until the day was over, or if we were lucky, until we found what we had been looking for. Buying the right horse was never easy.

Two weeks previously on a freezing February morning, I had flown back from sunny Brisbane. I had spent December and January working at a yard in the Southern Alps, and most of February training horses in the tropical heat in Caboolture. My head was full of training horses, and at the ripe old age of twenty-nine I wanted to buy myself a young horse to use the horsemanship I'd learned out in Australia and New Zealand. I was looking for a young green horse between 15 and 16 hands with good conformation, beautiful movement, not much done and a clean vet's cert. It would be like looking for a needle in a haystack but I knew if the right horse was here we would find him.

****

The ponies were being sold in the sales ring as Dad and I stood patiently outside in the yard, enjoying the warmth of the spring sun. Nearby, two mature ladies who had both seen their fair share of weather were leaning over the arena rails, each smoking a cigarette. The dark haired lady rested her arms on the wooden rails. She didn't look too happy.

'What did I tell you, he's a rough bugger that horse. He nearly killed me there last week. I showed him though,' she smiled bitterly. 'I'll be glad to see the back of him.'

Even in her glamorous green jacket, expensive gold watch and dark sunglasses, I got the feeling that you wouldn't want to meet her alone on a dark night. As she lifted her cigarette towards her mouth, I noticed her hard hands matched her horse. The streaky blond nodded in agreement.

'You're as well off. He needs a good sorting out. If I sell my two and we go home with an empty box this afternoon, I'll be happy.'

The blond was of fairly robust stock too.

'Yep. They seem to be selling so hopefully we'll be in luck,' the dark haired lady continued.

'I've had my eye on a four year old of Mark's down the road. Broken and riding, been out hunting and jumps likes a stag loose over a metre ten. I reckon if I can get him at the right price I might have him ready for Dublin next year.'

They paused to watch the bay jumping an oxer, and then the dark haired lady pushed her long fringe away, glanced at her watch and sighed.

'Come on, we better get going. We're jumping in half an hour in the indoor. I want to bring that horse out and run him over the practise fence outside a good few times to warm him up a bit. When he's gone it won't be a minute too soon.'

'Grand,' said the blonde, 'let's go.'

The two ladies walked off towards the stables, and were quickly lost amongst the milling crowd.

****

There wasn't much else happening in the yard and it was now approaching one o'clock. We had another good half hour to spare before the horses started to come out, so we decided it was time for lunch.

In the dining room the steam was heavy and rising as the ladies behind the counter carved industriously. We ordered our food, paid at the till and sat down. As conversation flowed around the room, the PA system from the nearby sales area mingled with the light smell of fresh horse manure. It was the usual mixture. Dealers with hard eyes, short arms and deep pockets, local farmers who bred a few horses to subsidise the farm, hunters, competition riders looking for new young stock, riding stable owners looking for suitable good value steeds and maybe something flash for themselves, and horses to be sold.

As we ate, I browsed through the photocopied catalogue pencilling in some of the young horses in the 15 hands to 16 hands category which were going to be sold later that day. The sales ring

3

was quite busy with ponies and a female dealer from England was doing a brisk trade in various models from her position at the perimeter of the sales ring. Many of the horses sold today would find their way across the Irish sea that night. The dining area was beginning to empty a little, and with our meal over it was time to head back out and look at some new bloodstock. A little skewbald pony, with the body of a twelve hand pony and the legs of a pony half that size, was making its way around the ring. It was probably the equine equivalent of a dachshund dog, but never the less extremely cute.

Amongst the animals in the yard we spotted a light fleabitten grey which according to the catalogue had very little done. According to the number on its rump, it was about to go into the ring for auction. Dad and I decided to go over for a look.

'Hi, how are you?' Dad introduced himself. The seller nodded and shook Dad's hand, then glanced towards me. He quickly assessed the situation and then shook my hand as well.

'Arra, I'm good thanks, you?' He had a Cork accent and wasn't slow off the ball.

'Yeah, grand thanks.' Dad looked more closely at the equine which stood in front of us. 'What kind of horse is this?' The horse wore a saddle and bridle and looked quiet enough.

'He's fifteen hands, grand horse, nice and quiet, he'll do everything. Been riding him myself'.

We took this knowledge with a pinch of salt.

'You wouldn't be able to trot him up for us?' We attempted to appear completely disinterested, as if we were only passing the time.

'Sure. You wouldn't be able to just wave him on a bit would you?' he replied.

'No worries,' Dad replied.

I stood to the side to watch the horse's movement as Dad jogged around behind the horse and started waving his arms towards the horse. After a few attempts the horse trotted on badly. His strides were fast and short. He was definitely not one of the most elegant movers amongst our list of potential prospects. I scratched his number out in the catalogue. We thanked the owner and then left the area. The whole procedure had taken less than two minutes.

****

As we walked back through the crowd, a steel grey horse wearing a saddle and bridle, with a number 24 sticker displayed on his rump, stood quietly near the entrance of the sales ring. At this stage the lot number being sold was approaching 40, so this little horse appeared to be lost. But then the only reason a horse will stand outside the ring is if someone is trying to sell him. On closer inspection he looked well put together, if a bit skinny. Dad and I walked up to his owner to see what the story was.

'How are ya?' Dad introduced himself and we both looked over the horse.

'Grand,' the owner replied, as he nodded at me. 'Not bad at all.' The owner tugged on the horse's lead rope, and the horse cautiously took a step over towards us.

'Emmm, has this horse been through the ring?' I asked, as I checked the catalogue. 'He's number 24 isn't he?'

The owner looked under pressure. He was about forty, business like, and in the usual attire of dealer boots, dark coloured trousers and a moderately worn coat. He took his cap off, wiped his forehead, put his cap back on again, sighed, and then looked directly at both of us. He had been around horses for a while.

'Aaahhh no, he hasn't been yet. We arrived late so we're going in after the next horse.' The grey horse stood patiently, looking past us towards the warm up arena.

'Oh right. What has he done?' I asked. He was a bit small for what I was looking for.

The owner replied: 'I bought him from a lad in Kilkenny six weeks ago with nothing done. He's a grand fella. Broke him in Wexford. He could do anything. Brave horse too.'

The last horse I heard was brave walked up onto a dung heap and jumped off over a wheelbarrow. I reckon if horses could talk they'd have some stories.

'Is he ok to handle?' I asked.

'Grand', the owner replied turning towards me. He held the lead rope tightly under the horses chin and then proceeded to rub the horse energetically around his head and ears. The horse didn't look too impressed and pulled against the tight lead rope but there was nowhere to go to.

'Nothing a bit of handling wouldn't sort out,' the man in the dealer boots informed us confidently.

He was probably right. But you would never guess that this horse couldn't be touched or caught, distrusted humans, was scared of everything, unridable, couldn't pick his feet up, bolted over all small fences and that even something as simple as putting on a headcollar was a major event. On a good note though, while the horse was small and skinny, his conformation wasn't bad so he was worth a look. Small horses tend to move like small horses so we weren't expecting much.

'You wouldn't mind just trotting him up for us, would you?' I asked politely, pointing towards the small rubber based track which had been built beside the stables.

6

'No bother at all, just give him a bit of a whoosh on to get him started,' the owner replied.

He led the horse over to the trotting lane and off the grey went without too much fuss. Our eyes opened wide as the horse trotted very nicely. It was an elegant trot, with lots of air and scope. This horse had potential I thought to myself. We immediately asked the owner to stop and come back over to us. We had seen the lovely movement, but we didn't want other people to see it too.

'Thanks for that…. aahh … he doesn't have a vet's cert by any chance?' I enquired.

'No he doesn't, but he's clean enough,' the owner replied. That was a pity I thought.

'Great, well good luck with him anyway,' we replied. We began walking back to the sales ring, with the images of the unassuming dark grey horse still in our heads. He was definitely a prospect. We just had to wait and see how much he started at in the ring. I crossed my fingers and circled his number in the catalogue.

Over the PA system the light fleabitten grey cob with the choppy movement was called into the ring. Out of curiosity we followed him in to see how well he would do. Five minutes later and he was sold for well over €3,000. On closer inspection of the catalogue it became clear why. Registered Irish Connemara. In his case the make was more important than the model.

As he waited in the ring, our steel grey horse walked in. Dad and I stood beside the sales ring, not saying a word, afraid we would give away our interest in buying this horse. I made myself concentrate on what the auctioneer said as my breathing got faster. Small, wide-eyed and nervous the grey walked anxiously around the sales ring, his front feet moving apprehensively through the fresh yellow sawdust. Bidding started quickly, with the English lady leading the buyers triumphantly from the ring side. €500 quickly turned into

€1000 and at €1500 he was officially on the market and would be sold. We quietly put in the next offer to the auctioneer's delight and after two or three more minutes of bidding, it was only us and the English dealer left as the price climbed higher. My heart was in my mouth.

'Going once, any more bids now'? The auctioneer's question rang around the room, crackling on the loudspeaker outside. I clenched my fists tightly and stopped breathing completely.

'Going twice, this is your last chance now……' the auctioneer paused, hammer raised, as I wished and hoped and prayed simultaneously. The auctioneer took a deep breath, as he glanced around the room and then shouted 'Sold!' exuberantly, as the hammer flew through the air and crashed down loudly onto the dark mahogany counter.

'To the lady at the ring. Well done madam,' the auctioneer articulated grandly in my direction.

The biggest smile spread across my face and I could have danced the whole way round the sales ring. The little grey horse was mine. The English dealer didn't seem too perturbed and was already inspecting the next horse in her catalogue.

To be brutally honest, aside from what the horse looked like, moved like, and his rough age, we weren't exactly sure what we had bought. Hopefully there wouldn't be too much physically wrong with him, and he had no obvious lumps or cuts. As he hadn't much done I hoped we wouldn't have too many problems when training him. It's easier to build a house on a clean patch of ground than to have to demolish the old house that's there first. Or that was my theory.

'Well done!' Dad said, grinning at me, and also delighted. 'He could be anything but he's got potential.' I was still beaming. 'I can't believe it!' I replied. 'I was sure that English lady was going to

8

outbid us. Let's sort out the money and head back out and have another look at him.'

We went into the office, signed the forms and handed over a cheque for the sale price plus commission and VAT, and then headed back to stable 24 to see exactly what we had just bought. We opened the bolt on the wooden door of the stable and peered into the gloomy interior.

Inside, crouched right at the back was the little grey horse. He wasn't much to look at, huddled flat against the white washed wall. A few attempts to offer him a hand to smell didn't go well. It just resulted in him moving even further away from us so we figured he was a bit shy. As we closed his door I saw his previous owner walking up the yard with another horse to sell. That was the last time we saw him, so I never found out the new horse's name. I would have to give him a new one.

Dad and I had driven up from Tipperary that morning without a horsebox, not really expecting to see a horse we liked. At this stage it was about 3pm so we figured the best idea would be to drive home, pick up the horsebox and then be back for about six or half six to collect the horse.

Three and a half hours later with our horsebox in tow and headlights on, we turned into the empty car park beside the sales complex. It was turning dusk and except for one solitary jeep in the yard, there was no other sign of life at all. The whole sales complex was shut and our little horse was somewhere in the middle of it - padlocked into his dark stable.

We headed back up the village, and as we drove down the main street, a dark saloon car drove up beside us and decelerated. A window was electronically rolled down in our direction.

'Are ye alright there?' the unknown driver enquired, peering into our car.

9

'Oh grand yes thanks. We're actually looking to get into the horse sales, we've a horse to pick up in there'. Luckily he didn't seem too surprised.

We had just stumbled across one of the guys who worked in the sales yard, who had been curious about why a horsebox was wandering around the town looking lost, two hours after everyone else had gone home.

Kindly he agreed to meet us back at the yard and open up the gates for us to get our horse. Ten minutes later, we opened the stable door and inside our little horse was waiting. Putting on the halter in the small stable took about three minutes as he artfully evaded all human touches. He was very nervous.

Dad led him out through the empty moonlit stable yards, and the grey walked on lightly, loading into the box without too much hesitation. With gratitude for our gate opener we began the journey back home. The little horse stood quietly the whole way, and not once did we feel the car suspension move. You wouldn't have known he was there at all.

An hour and a half later we arrived home and unloaded the horse without incident. As I led the grey down the horsebox ramp I wanted to rub his shoulder, but his whole body was telling me that he absolutely didn't want me to do that. He didn't have a very high opinion of humans. I silently accepted the challenge and lead him into the stable without touching him. I undid the halter and he immediately moved away from me as I closed the stable door.

'He does have a handsome head doesn't he?' Dad remarked as he unhitched the horsebox.

'Yes, I think so. I can't wait until I can start working with him. I'll give him a few days outside first to get used to the place and then we'll see what we will do. I'll take it slowly anyway.'

As I looked at the grey over the stable door, the realisation of having my own young horse to bring on began to hit me. I started to realise how much of a responsibility this grey horse was going to be.

It took me hours that night to fall asleep, as training ideas and pictures of the grey filled my thoughts.

The grey horse had a new home.

02. Untouchable

The next day the horse stayed true to form. Any attempt to offer a hand to smell was met with rapid movement towards the back of the stable. If he was already back there, he would expertly turn his neck and head fully around to the far side where you couldn't see it, let alone try to rub it. To be honest from what I had already seen, I knew this horse was worried. My first challenge would be to prove to him that he did not need to be.

As I walked into the yard I could see his head looking out over the stable door. As I neared the stable, he eyed me suspiciously and withdrew his head. Then he casually moved over to eat some hay which was lying on the ground at the front of the stable. I watched him for a while and he seemed pretty quiet. But he still wouldn't come back over to the door where I stood.

Slowly, I undid the two latches and opened the stable door a little. The grey regarded me with distain and moved away from the hay, back towards the rear of the stable. I slipped into the stable and closed the door quietly behind me. The new horse maintained a safe distance away from me.

'Hello little fella,' I murmured under my breath while staying where I was. 'You've nothing to worry about.'

He looked at me with contempt written all over his face, not believing a word I said. He wasn't trembling, sweating or anxious and he didn't look scared. He just looked like he would prefer if I wasn't there. I was starting to realise that this horse wasn't the clean slate I had thought I had bought.

I picked up some hay and held it out to him. He regarded me calmly. 'You don't really think I'm going to eat that now, do you?' His body language communicated his thoughts very clearly. It was his choice whether he wanted to eat or not, so that was fair enough.

'That's alright little guy,' I replied. 'It's up to you. Let's try a little patience instead.'

I watched him closely. He wasn't scared, just a bit wary. I side-stepped to the right until I stood right in front of the hay. Then I waited.

The grey looked at me for a few minutes, trying to figure out what I was doing. He took a step closer towards the hay, and I immediately looked away from him. You could nearly hear him thinking 'WHAT is she doing standing beside MY hay?'

He did want some hay, so he took a step to the side looking for a direct route to the food which wouldn't involve moving too close towards me. I watched him calmly and then took a half step in the same direction.

He looked at me crossly, and then moved a step the other way. Then so did I. After a few more attempts, the grey looked at me, frustration written all over his face as if to say 'That's MY HAY you know!' and stamped his foot in disgust.

He was a character! Clever, intelligent and with a mind of his own I reckoned. To confirm my suspicions, I picked up some hay in my hand. I stood where I was, stretched out my arm slowly towards him and offered him the hay. The horse regarded my arm with disdain and remained at his position at the back of the stable. He didn't trust me and whatever he thought I was going to do to him he didn't like it. I wanted to put him in the front paddock with Pepsi our retired pony who would be acting as his babysitter. Unfortunately if he hated being touched, he would be impossible to catch. With the nights still quite cold and frosty, he would need to come in as he was currently sporting a nice trace clip.

13

I opened the door and slipped back out of the stable. Once the door was firmly closed, the grey warily took a few steps towards the front of the stable and resumed eating his hay, giving me his best *'I'm not impressed'* look. I had wanted to leave him alone for his first few days to settle in, but this wouldn't work. I had to be able to catch him. I needed a plan.

****

Five minutes later I walked back into the kitchen and sat down at the table. Mum was preparing vegetables for dinner, amidst an ongoing breakfast and the Sunday papers. Friends of ours had been invited over for lunch and preparations for the occasion had turned our usually relaxed kitchen table into a strategic planning centre.

'Morning, you're up early.' Several pots and pans were already stacked up, ready for use. Mum was busy.

'I was just out with the new horse,' I replied. 'He's a bit nervous. He doesn't want to be touched and if you go near him he sticks to the back wall like glue.'

Mum looked at me with raised eyebrows. 'Oh right. Well you've got a good project then.' I nodded my head in agreement and poured some orange juice.

'I think so,' I replied as I polished off the juice. 'He looks fine anyway. He ate a fair bit of hay which is good. I'll have to do a bit of work with him now before I let him out.'

I started to butter a scone. 'There's not a hope I could throw on a saddle and get up though, he'd flip out I'd say. He needs a bit of time and handling.'

Mum looked over at me. 'Right. I guess that means you are on the washup after lunch!'

14

'If that's ok, yes,' I replied with a grin. 'I want to do a bit of work with the horse this morning and see if I can start to figure him out.' I was never very good at preparing vegetables anyway.

The morning flew past and soon it was 1.30pm and time for lunch. Our friends had arrived over so it was time to eat and catch up.

****

Two hours, three courses and one very quick washup later, I headed back out to the stables to continue work with the grey. A few minutes later, I heard the lock on the back door of the house squeak open, and soon four curious faces were peering over the stable door.

Mum, Dad, Frank and Deirdre were greeted with the sight of a large dummy arm, complete with a multi-coloured gardening glove with faux leather trimming, being rubbed by me on a nervous looking horse who was standing anxiously at the back of the stable, ears pointed backwards. What on earth had I bought, and what on earth was I doing with a fake arm?

My plan involved the resurrection of a device which I had made the previous year in Sligo. It consisted of the finest Dunnes Stores mop handle (minus the mop itself), the arm of a mens size navy blue jumper, and a large gardening glove all stuck together to look like a human arm. The way it worked was that starting at his shoulder, I'd rub him for a few seconds. If he stood still, then I'd stop rubbing him and then move away, to reward his good behaviour. If he moved or started to walk about, then I'd just keep rubbing him.

'God Elaine, but that's an unusual looking thing you have there.' Frank was as direct as he was droll.

'It's called how to touch a horse without getting kicked!' I replied chuckling. 'He must have had a bit of rough handling before as he really doesn't want to be anywhere near people.'

15

I had done about four short sessions so far that day with the grey horse, and at the minute he would stand still while I rubbed his back and shoulder with the fake hand.

'He's a nice looking horse though.' Frank paused for a moment as he gathered his thoughts. 'Just watch out for the wet cement.'

'The wet cement?' said Dad puzzled. 'What do you mean?' We all turned to look at Frank, as Deirdre started to giggle.

'All I'm saying,' said Frank as he paused for effect, 'is don't drag your feet. A bit of handling like you said and he will turn inside out quite quickly.' Frank grinned and nodded his head in confirmation.

'I wish you the very best of luck with him Elaine, he'll be a grand horse. Sure doesn't he have you to teach him!' Frank had heard some of my horse stories from Australia.

'Thanks Frank,' I grinned back.

****

By 4pm that afternoon I had made some progress. With some difficulty I put on a headcollar and led the grey out to the small paddock where our retired pony was waiting. The new horse walked nervously on the end of the lead rope with short anxious steps. He was understandably spooky.

I left him off in the paddock, with his headcollar still on, something I don't normally do. After a bit of walking about and looking, the grey horse suddenly started to canter, buck and kick like a madman.

'Would you look at him go!' Dad said as the grey kung-fued his way around the paddock like a master fighter from an international Asian martial arts movie.

16

'Jackie Chan has nothing on this guy,' I replied, raising both eyebrows. 'I'm just glad I'm not in the saddle yet!'

Our pony also looked on in disbelief at the raving lunatic who'd just invaded his paddock. A few minutes later with the initial excitement over, Pepsi and the grey were grazing and so we left them together as the sun dipped behind the trees. The Sunday papers were calling. It had been a long and interesting day.

The grey wasn't the relatively well adjusted ridden horse he had been sold as, but I enjoy a challenge. He had spirit and opinions and he was definitely going to need time and patience and lots of work to get him going nicely.

I figured that if I could instill good boundaries and show him he could trust and be happy around people, he might turn into a well adjusted sociable horse.

We would just have to wait and see.

03. How long does it take to catch a horse?

On a dull Novembers day, as the clouds gathered overhead and the rain began to fall lightly down on the already waterlogged fields, a middle aged lady knocked timidly on the brown front door of the local parish house. The house itself was an old building, full of long corridors and creaky stairs. After a short wait, the wooden door inched open slowly and the priest peered out into the gloomy weather.

'Hello Father' she said, 'I wonder if you can help me?' The woman paused, tightening the coat around her as the wind danced in circles.

'Oh hello Mrs. Kelly, the priest replied warmly, 'come inside and let me know what I can do for you. You're just in time, the kettle's just boiled.'

Two minutes later Mrs. Kelly was firmly ensconced in the sitting room, a cup of tea in her hand and a warm fire in front of her.

'Now Mrs. Kelly, what can I do for you?', the priest enquired. Mrs. Kelly looked across at him, wrinkling her forehead, carefully arranging the delivery of her next words.

'Well Father', she began hesitantly, 'I have a bit of a problem.' She nervously fidgeted with the strap on her well worn bag. She looked up at the priest as the wrinkles in her brows deepened. She was a worried woman.

'I've just found out that I've won the euro millions – forty million euros,' she said rushing over her words, 'but I don't know how I'll tell Bill. He's got a weak heart and I'm afraid that he'll get a heart attack when I tell him.' 'Oh' said the priest thoughtfully. Bill and Mary had never missed a Sunday mass in the last thirty years. 'I

18

see your predicament alright', the priest replied, nodding his head sagely.

'What I was wondering' Mrs. Kelly continued, plucking up her courage along with her handbag, 'is if you could break the news to him? I think he'd take it better from you.'

The priest's eyebrows raised themselves up towards his forehead, and his mouth formed itself into a perfect 'O'. This was definitely one of the more unusual requests he had come across in his role as God's representative in this little parish.

'No bother at all,' he replied, good-humouredly. 'I'll call up tomorrow morning and we'll have a chat' he finished, and relief spread quickly across Mrs. Kelly's face.

'Oh Father, you're great. I knew I could count on you', she said, thrilled to have the worry lifted from her mind. 'Thank you very much Father'.

'The priest smiled. 'Not at all, you're most welcome Mrs. Kelly. I'll see you back out to your car.'

****

The next morning, the priest had arrived at the Kelly's house and Bill answered the door.

'Come in Father, what can I do for you?' he asked, ushering the priest into the house. 'Oh thank you Bill, just a social call I'm afraid. How is everyone these days?' the priest enquired.

'Oh very well thanks Father,' Bill replied. 'You've just missed Mary, she's gone into town for the messages. Come inside here to the kitchen, and I'll put on some tea.'

The priest followed Mr. Kelly into the kitchen, and sat down beside the kitchen table. Soon the kettle had boiled, and the conversation which had begun with the weather, travelled onto gaelic football and then cattle prices, and was now moving onto more pressing matters.

The priest cocked his head and looked over towards Bill. He leaned over across the table. 'Can I ask you a question Bill?' the priest enquired, his eyes fixed on Bill's clear honest expression.

'Oh course you can indeed' Bill replied, wondering what was about to come.

The priest leaned forward a little more. 'What would you do Bill, if you won the lotto?'

Bill leaned back in his chair and smiled broadly. 'Well Father, sure that would be easy. I'd give it all to you.'

The priests face went grey, and he fell from his chair onto the floor. He was underground three days later.

****

Horses are like winning the lotto. They can do something unexpected which makes you feel like you're walking on clouds. Or if you're unlucky they can do something equally unexpected which lands you on the flat of your back. You have to try to keep your wits about you as much as possible.

****

On Monday morning the new horse seemed quite happy out in the paddock with Pepsi. The weather was due to get a bit colder that night, so I was anxious to bring him in that evening to his stable.

That afternoon, the sky darkened as clouds gathered and the rain arrived once more. Soon the rain was driving in sideways accompanied by a wind that would tear the skin off your bones. After putting on as many coats, gloves and hats as I could find, I headed out into the bad weather to begin the arduous task of catching the new horse.

I knew it wouldn't be too easy, so I had already decided to make things more straightforward by bringing in Pepsi earlier, leaving the halter on the new horse, and having him in a relatively small paddock. I estimated that catching the new horse would take fifteen or possibly twenty minutes.

Three very long wet hours later, I was soaked through from the lashing rain and my jeans had turned from light blue to dark black. There were puddles in my boots, and a river reminiscent of the Shannon in flood ran from the peak of my hat down over my face and descended with gravity down my soaked jacket. Half of me was cold, wet and resigned to my fate, and the other half was cold and wet and determined. The grey and I were still out there.

I could get relatively close to him at times, but once I breached his 'safety zone' he would turn and walk away from me. When he walked away, I would flap my arms and push him away. Horses tend to get fed up of being pushed around and they'll stand quietly. But this guy had other ideas. Catching a horse that can't be touched is quite a difficult thing to try to do.

But there was no point getting stressed about something I couldn't control, so I just smiled and kept at it. Unfortunately for my new horse I was born just as stubborn as he was. Eventually, for a reason I am not aware of, the grey stood still for a second and allowed me to clip the lead rope to his halter. Maybe he felt sorry for me or had eventually gotten bored with the game. Once caught, I led him in quietly to the stables. He led perfectly on a loose rein, not once pulling on the lead rope. It was the one thing he could actually do. I knew he wasn't going to be easy, but this had been a particularly long evening.

After that, things started to look up. For the next three or four days, I let the new horse out every morning and brought him in every evening. At the time I had started to look for an I.T. job again, so for the next two months I lived at home and Ozzie was basically my full time job. We did a lot of work together during this time.

Twice a day every day, I would spend five or ten minutes with the dummy arm, and later with my own arm, rubbing from his shoulder to his lower neck, upper neck, and then back and rump. It was slow progress, but I enjoyed it a lot. You could see little improvements each day, and the more time I spent with the grey, the more I figured out what was going on in his head. We were gradually learning about each other, and he was giving me lots to think about.

Putting on his headcollar was still very tricky as he was very head shy and didn't like me anywhere near his face. I would put my hand near his face, or high up on his neck, and when he stood still, I'd take my hand away as a reward. When he moved his head, I'd stay with him. You could nearly hear his brain working. He had a very low opinion of people but he was a quick learner.

At this stage his legs and nose and mouth were still absolutely off limits. While we were getting better putting on the headcollar, we still had a long way to go.

Every day the grey had been getting slowly better with the halter. Because of this, the catching was improving as well, and now I could leave him out in the small paddock without a headcollar. It took about ten minutes to catch him now, which was a huge improvement on where we had started. We were heading in the right direction, and the idea that this horse could trust me had started to wander through his mind.

Pepsi found it hard to eat short grass as his front teeth weren't great due to his age and the new horse needed some condition. As their paddock was beginning to look a little bare, it was nearly time to put both of them out in the big field. I couldn't keep calling him 'the grey' though. He needed a name.

****

'What are you going to call him? He's got to have a name you know'. My brother was curious. He'd heard about my new horse on the phone the night before.

'I don't know…….. I was thinking of Ozzie maybe,' I replied. While he was Irish on the outside, I planned on using a mixture of Australian and Irish methods to bring him on.

'That's cool, like Ozzie Osbourne yeah?' My brother was delighted. The new horse was going to be a rocker.

'Emm,' I replied. 'Not quite.'

'That's a cool name for a horse Elaine, definitely go with that'.

So it was settled. Ozzie it was.

****

Soon enough, it was time to put both horses out in the big field. On Sunday, one week after I bought him, we led them both down, took off their headcollars and watched as they wandered off slowly. Pepsi put his head down immediately and Ozzie snatched at grass as he trotted up the hill exploring his new home. It was a beautiful afternoon and Ozzie looked relaxed and very pleased with himself. It was lovely watching him moving around the field.

Ozzie really did have a mind of this own though. Only time would tell if I could catch him again.

04. Moving forwards and going backwards

As we sat in the spacious room the gentle hum of the lawn mower and the bird song outside drifted into us. The lecturer was busy sorting out music at the top of the room, so we chatted amongst ourselves. It was a class of about twenty, and it ran the way all classes should - interesting, educational and thought provoking. The lecturer fiddled with the stereo a bit more and then turned back around to us.

'Ok, no talking please. I'm going to play three pieces of music and I'd like you to write down the era and composer for each with reasons please.'

Soon works by Scarlatti, Mendelssohn and Puccini filled the room and flowed out through the high open windows across the lawns and towards the computer labs. You could never call something like this work.

Studying music makes you think and listen a lot. When you play the piano at college level it is not so much about what you play, but how you play it. You press the notes, then listen and analyse what sound you created, and then use this information to shape what you are creating into something unique and special. Three years later I found myself in a dusty central Dublin underground rehearsal studio, a member of our renowned 'fuse blowing' (yes literally) cover band. Our glorious leader / musical director had the undeniable patience of a saint and was fairly blunt. He was in charge of getting us all into some form of musical shape. We'd been rehearsing for an hour at this stage.

'Spinal tap hasn't a patch on us!' he roared. 'Ok let's do it again. There's still too many bloody guitars. And who's making that awful noise??!!!!' It sounded like there was a small animal being killed.

He threw he eyes up to heaven and then caught sight of the offending culprit.

'Jason, for the last time can you please stop playing that bloody country music. I'm not telling you anymore. Right, from the top everyone. One, two, three, go!!!'

At the time I was working fulltime as a sound engineer in a software company in Dublin, and whatever parts of my ears were left after playing 'Five Hundred Miles' at a substantial volume with nine other highly enthusiastic musicians, every day I would have to listen carefully to voiceover artists enunciating every syllable for our elearning cd-roms. I had to be good at listening and analysing. It was a lot like horses really.

If you look at a horse you normally see a head, four legs and a tail. Watching a horse actively involves a bit more. What is his conformation like? How is he moving? Is his attention focused on something else? Why has he just moved that ear? Are his shoulders braced? Are his ribs soft? Is his neck tense? Is he about to get spooked? Is he worried and anxious? Is he paying any attention to me? Was that a slight give? Did he soften a fraction just then?

People talk about how important feel and timing is with horses and they're right. But you've got to be able to look and listen first. All you need is a willingness to learn and as much practise as you can get. Luckily the best horse teachers in the world come on four legs.

****

When I bought Ozzie he was sporting a professional looking clip which included half of his face, a rash on his back, a pulled mane, clipped bridle path and a full set of shoes one size too small. From what I'd seen of him so far, how anyone got to him to stand while being clipped or while holding his feet up was a mystery to me. I had a few theories though and I would bet money it wasn't done

25

with Ozzie's cooperation. So I had decided to take the 'broken and riding' part with a pinch of salt too. If you try to get up on a horse that has no trust in humans and is already very worried about what's happening, you might just find yourself getting off fairly quick. My plan was a complete restart of Ozzie to put in all the foundations which were missing. How long it was going to take would depend on Ozzie. Currently this little horse didn't believe in anyone but himself.

****

That night Ozzie was quite good. Because he was now out in the field, I had given myself an hour of evening light before dusk to catch him. After about forty five minutes he was being led back up towards the stables.

The next day after a little more handling, I was standing outside his stable door untangling the halter to get it ready to put on him. Ozzie was standing at the far side of the stable door looking on with interest.

As I worked, I slowly became aware of a large grey nose which had begun to inch its way over the stable door, towards the peak of my baseball hat. I held my breath as I continued to fiddle with the halter, not daring to move a muscle. I couldn't believe what was happening. The grey nose came closer and sniffed my hat gingerly. About three or four seconds later with the 'hat' investigation complete, the grey nose then quietly disappeared back into the stable.

This was the first time in the ten days with me that Ozzie had shown any kind of positive interest in a human. I couldn't help myself as a big grin spread across my face. This was huge progress! It probably took about twenty hours of handling to get here but who was counting?

Ozzie was beginning to come out of his shell a little and his evasions and fears were slowly being replaced with curiosity. The prospect of a saddle and bridle was definitely still a long way away and we had a lot of very basic work to do before then which hadn't been done in his first five years.

'Dad, you'll never believe what happened!' I was literally hopping off the ground at this stage.

Dad threw his eyes up to heaven and smiled. 'Go on'.

'The new horse put his head over the door and sniffed my hat! That's the first time he's even done anything like that.'

'That's great' Dad replied smiling. 'He's coming on. All he needs is a bit of time. Well done, that's great.'

I was bursting with happiness. Later that morning, I left him back in the field with Pepsi, feeling quite happy with the progress to date. With hindsight I should have realised that something was due to go badly wrong.

****

That night the forecast was for clear skies and cold weather. I headed out as usual an hour before dusk to catch Ozzie. Our resident guard dog who resembled a large glamorous sheep was in top form. Galloping about at the start of the field with the wind running through his hair, he was like something you'd see in a high-class ladies shampoo advertisement on television. You could hear the strings soaring above the full wind and brass sections, as he moved in slow motion, cymbals crashing, as his glorious mane shone and danced in the wind.

At the other end of the field, a herd of young cattle had taken up position at the gap and were peering in, eyes wide in interest and anticipation at the two horses next door.

As I approached Ozzie he moved away from me, so I whooshed him off again as usual. Such were the magnitude of the distractions, with the dog galloping about at one end of the field and the cattle standing like unearthly creatures at the other end, that Ozzie spent the next forty five minutes trotting, cantering and galloping with his neck arched and tail up like an Arabian stallion, moving at speed from one end of the field to another. He made a pretty picture but I couldn't catch him. As the light decreased, I had to admit defeat and gave up. Ozzie wasn't going to be caught that evening. Despondent under the light of the rising moon, I walked slowly back in through the empty paddock, and arrived back at the house as darkness fell. I slowly returned the unused headcollar to its hook and took off my boots and unbuttoned my coat. The plan had gone wrong somewhere along the way. He was getting more difficult.

'Did you get him in alright? It's going to be a bit chilly out there tonight,' Mum commented from inside the newspaper.

'No,' I replied despondently. 'Ozzie got excited with the dog and the cattle and he galloped around like a lunatic. I had to leave him out there.'

I knew he would be alright but I was a bit disappointed. I really couldn't bear to go back to our three hour catching sessions.

'Don't worry, these things happen. See what he's like tomorrow' Mum replied.

'Yep, that's all I can do really.' I went into the lounge and sat down beside the warm open fire. If Ozzie wanted to stay out in the cold then that was ok. But rather him than me.

****

The next morning I had a few things to buy in Limerick, so it was well after lunch before I got a chance to check on the horses. As I walked down the path our other two horses Cinders and Dougal wandered over to say hello. In the distance, I could see Ozzie and Pepsi happily eating grass. The thought reoccurred to me that perhaps I should have done more than one week's handling with Ozzie. But given the situation, he really had to go out to the big field and I'd done as much work with him as I could in the given time. Catching this little horse was never supposed to be easy.

As I approached the end of the path beside the entrance to the field, Ozzie caught sight of me. He raised his head into the air, looked straight at me and pricked his ears forwards towards me.

'Elaine, there you are!! Where did you go?'

Two seconds later Ozzie broke into a nice easy trot and headed straight down to me, stopping at the field entrance where I stood. He stood beside me without a care in the world as I rubbed his near shoulder and the part of his face he was comfortable with. That meant a lot to me. Ozzie and I were back on track.

05. Two weeks: building confidence and a plan

Overall Ozzie had progressed a lot in the two weeks he had spent in Tipperary. I had been working with him for about two hours over a few sessions every day and he had started to become friendly and sociable with me, though he was still very wary of other people. Most importantly he was now pretty easy to catch in a large field without the need for any props or complicated forward planning. Handling his nose and legs was still an issue, but they were improving slowly.

My end goal was to be the proud owner of a nice well adjusted soft and responsive ridden horse and we had started well. I needed all the basics in place before I could move onto the more advanced tasks like saddling and riding.

My horse had to be happy and relaxed around people and be easy to handle and touch all over. The plan was that Ozzie would also have to do all the foundation work well, including being easy to catch, lead, shoe and load. Just as importantly, this basic training had to succeed in convincing Ozzie that people were friendly, fun, safe and had to be respected and obeyed at all times. Trust and teamwork were being improved at this stage, and they would be needed later when saddling, riding and doing more complex tasks. For me, trust is using the knowledge of what happened in the past to predict what will happen in the future. I wanted to build a good relationship between us on the ground and build Ozzie's trust in me. When I got into the saddle, I wanted him to trust that I'd listen to him, take care of him, never push him too hard and never use violence against him. Trust runs both ways.

Secondly, I needed to get Ozzie used to all the things he would come across as a grown up horse. This would initially include ropes, sticks, poles, fences, uprights, walking over strange ground (mimicking a horse box floor or walking through water) walking backwards (unloading from a horsebox), walking through gaps, plastic bags, umbrellas, quads, cars, dogs and bicycles. I would also need to include all of the riding materials – girths, numnahs, saddle and stirrups.

Thirdly, I wanted to prepare Ozzie for basic ridden work. I wanted a horse who was soft, supple and responsive. I wanted a horse who accepted the bit, had the lightest of mouths, perfect brakes and could do lateral work well. Ozzie would be ridden mainly from seat cues, and should be able to carry himself correctly with free moving shoulders, vertical flexion and hindquarter engagement. He would also need lateral flexion to be able to move around a circle and as an Irish horse he should be well able to jump fences in style. In essence I wanted a brave confident performance horse anyone would be proud to own. And we were going to do it all using the lightest of cues, without too many gadgets. I wanted to keep it simple. To achieve this Ozzie would be learning a lot of groundwork, which would teach him everything from brakes and hindquarter yields, to working correctly on a circle with softness and flexion. When Ozzie was confident, trusting and used to numnahs, saddles and stirrups, I'd sit in the saddle.

Our basic handling was coming along well now, with catching and some touching done. Ozzie was now also letting me touch his mouth and nose happily, which was a direct result of his new found confidence and acceptance of me. With leading not an issue, our last hurdle in this area was touching his legs and then picking up his feet in preparation for our farrier, who had been out the previous week to do our other horses.

****

'His heels were a bit long alright, but he'll be grand now,' Joseph said conversationally, rasp in hand.

'He's a bit more arthritic these days isn't he' I replied, as Pepsi sighed deeply. I gave him a rub on his forehead and he gently lowered his head. At thirty he was the respected gentleman of our

31

horses. I had spent many glorious days galloping around on his back jumping everything in sight when I was younger and even now he still had a mind of his own.

'He's a bit stiff alright,' Joseph replied with a nod of his head. 'We had an old mare who was a lot worse. She found it hard to lift her leg out, but I got a brick and she'd stand on that and you could work around her no bother.'

So there was hope for Pepsi yet anyway. His official passport put him at thirty years of age, but to be honest that's probably a conservative guess. Paper never refused ink.

'I bought a new horse there recently. A little grey fella.' I added, looking out towards the field.

'Oh did you now.' Joseph looked up to me with interest. If I knew half of what Joseph's forgotten I'd be happy.

'Yeah, he's a grand fella. A bit wild though,' I added, trying not to smile and waiting to see Joseph's reaction. He stopped rasping and looked up at me through raised eyebrows. I don't think farriers like shoeing wild horses.

'It's fine, he doesn't need to be shod today,' I continued quickly, smiling. 'He's got four new shoes on him, and I have a lot of work to do with him before I'd ask anyone to pick up his feet!' Joseph looked relieved and I don't blame him. I wouldn't like to shoe a wild horse either.

'Oh grand, I was wondering alright' he replied with a wry grin, and then launched into a few colourful horror stories of wild horses and ponies who were presented to him to shoe. It was usually only after the horse was done that the owner would come up, slap him on the back and say:

'Fair play to you now, that horse only came off the bog in Kerry yesterday. You're some man alright.'

32

06. Tread softly for you tread on my carpet

Last year I walked into a flooring showroom on the outskirts of Sligo town. Carpets of every make, variety and colour were displayed artistically around the showroom. Couples were wandering around 'oohing' and 'aahing' while comparing prices, colour and depth against mix and wool percentages. There were a few bored looking partners, probably pulled away from a football match on television. I looked across the room and caught the eye of one of the sales guys and he quickly made his way to where I stood.

'Hello, how can I help you?' He was businesslike and efficient in his grey pin stripe suit.

'Hello, I'm emm…. just wondering if you'd have any spare pieces of carpet that you wouldn't need……I'm looking for it for a horse,' I ended lamely. I watched bewilderment followed quickly by amusement growing across the sales guy's face. He had a right tulip here.

'For a horse?!' he repeated, assuming he hadn't heard me correctly.

'Ah yes' I replied, 'I train horses and I need to teach a horse to walk over something strange as part of his training.'

The sales guy started grinning, his eyes lighting up. I imagine there weren't many people who had come through those doors with this particular request.

'Ahhh, leave it with me for a minute I'll see what I can do', he said as he sauntered away to confer with one of the managers. I stood near a delightful flower patterned creation, and continued to turn a deeper shade of fuchsia, matching some of the nearby carpets nicely.

The sales people exchanged words, and the manager looked a bit puzzled. Then he turned back to the sales guy again to continue their conversation. After some head nodding, the sales guy was dispatched to the back of the warehouse and after a few minutes he duly reappeared with a large rectangular orange carpet. He walked back up to me smiling impishly.

'What would you think of this? Would it do the trick? Is the colour alright?'

With a beautiful rosy red face, I assured him that the colour was perfect and that the carpet was of a suitable size for my horse to stand upon. When I offered to carry it out to my car, the sales guy absolutely insisted on lifting it out for me, and two minutes later had reverentially placed it in the boot of my car. At this stage, word had got round so there was now a small audience watching us. I thanked him profusely, back-peddled into my car, and drove off smiling with my red face still intact. The things we do for horses.

Since then, the carpet had travelled well from Sligo down to Tipperary, and so it was brought out to the field and deposited on the ground as Ozzie watched intently from half way up the field.

'What the bloody hell is THAT Elaine?!' It was definitely weird.

Horses are curious creatures and this is really useful when getting them used to new things. There are lots of ways of doing this. One way I like is the desensitisation approach. Basically you break it down into small parts and then let your horse do the work in his own time. Good behaviour is rewarded by rests and the scary thing or the horse (whichever is more practical in the situation) is taken away.

At the beginning I didn't want Ozzie to walk on the carpet, I just wanted him to be near it. I walked up the field to catch Ozzie and he stood there quietly, engrossed by the distant orange object.

'I have NEVER seen anything like that in my life before!!'

Horses feel braver if someone walks between them and the scary object so I had myself positioned on his far side in between Ozzie and the 'unexplored as of yet' carpet. I quietly led him down towards it on a loose rein.

As he got closer to the carpet, he suddenly stood as still as a rock with all four legs planted under him, breathing faster.

He stared intently upon the unearthly orange flooring which had invaded his field. It could have been from a foreign galaxy and definitely looked like it would kill him!

So Ozzie didn't want to get any nearer yet and that was fine by me. Instead we started to walk in a larger arc around the carpet, with me between him and the carpet still on a loose rein. After a minute or two without any protest from him I was able to subtly start making the circle slightly smaller.

After about four minutes of this, we were walking around the perimeter of the carpet, Ozzie being very relaxed and laid back about the whole thing. For me it wasn't so much that he would be able to walk over the carpet, rather that he would be happy to. I was training his mind more than his body.

After another minute or two, Ozzie started to display interest in standing at the carpets edge, sniffing it. I just stood and waited.

'Gosh, is this 100% wool mix? Wow I'm impressed Elaine!'

After another minute or two, Ozzie started to get playful and began nibbling on the carpet's edge. He'd pull on it and make it jump and rush back, then look a bit sheepish and walk up to it again pretending nothing had happened. I did my best to pretend to be serious as well!

Soon we'd gone from scary horse to playful horse. He'd sniff it as far as he could, right into the centre of it, and then casually place a front foot on the carpet edge.

After a few minutes Ozzie had his two feet on the carpet, so then before he had it completely pulled apart I asked him to walk over it to the grass at the other side. No problem at all.

Five minutes later and we could walk over the carpet from all angles, stop on it, and backup from it. Job done.

The more time I spent with Ozzie the more hopeful I became. We were progressing slowly, but we were headed in the right direction.

07. The brakes

When I was in university in Kildare our riding club had arranged weekly sessions for our competition riders at a good local riding centre near the college. It was always nice to go horse riding during the week and it was usually followed by an equally good session in the local pub afterwards. Because it was normally dark by the time we arrived at the yard, our lessons would take place in a large indoor arena. We'd put on our hats, pick up our assigned horses, lead them down to the indoor school, jump on and then get a lesson in dressage or jumping.

At that time we were preparing for the national intervarsities. This was a national level Irish student equestrian competition involving dressage and showjumping on unknown horses. It was regarded in equal measure for its social attributes (a pound a pint during its heyday) as well as its high level of equestrian expertise. Each college was invited to field a team of nine people – three in dressage, three in showjumping and three in prix caprilli.

To make things equal for all, everyone had to ride an unknown horse when competing. There might be three people riding one particular horse in the dressage competition, and so you would be scored against the other people riding that same horse. It really was a fair test of riding ability. Rather than placing the emphasis on who owned the best trained or most expensive horse, the winner was the best rider. We had won the competition the previous year to the delight of our university sports officer and disbelief of my music professor and we were honoured to host the event that year, which we did in great style outside Naas, Co. Kildare.

This particular evening, the riding school had kindly set up a show jumping course for us in about three quarters of the indoor arena. The rest of the arena had been fenced off, so the other people on horseback could stand quietly and watch the rounds without

37

getting in the way. I was riding a big dark thoroughbred type horse who had seemed relatively normal.

What I do remember clearly about this evening is the showjumping course. I had jumped one or two of the fences fine, and then suddenly my horse started to canter faster and faster. I tried pulling on his mouth, but got no reaction from the horse. I tried turning him through the fences to slow him down, but it was no good. He just kept getting faster and faster, and soon we had moved up into a gallop. The horse had the bit clamped between his teeth and for whatever reason, was intent on seriously injuring both himself and myself that night. Sitting up in that saddle at something over twenty five miles an hour I was dreading how it would end.

Soon the horse had got so fast that I had no option but to keep him steered out on the perimeter of the indoor arena. If I'm riding a bolting horse, I would normally turn them in a circle and wait for them to slow down. However, most of the arena was filled with fences. If I had tried to turn the horse in a circle, we would have crashed at speed into a fence. And it wouldn't have been pretty.

As the instructor and the other students looked on in horror from their end of the arena (there were a few white faces along with my own that night) my horse continued to gallop around the arena like the devil was after him. He'd gallop along the short side, maintain his speed going around the corner, increase his speed on the long side, maintain that speed going around the corner and the short side, and then increase his speed again each time he hit the long side of the arena. Sitting in the saddle I couldn't see how this could have a good ending. If we kept doing this we were going to crash soon at a full gallop, straight into the concrete wall. We were in trouble.

How I eventually stopped that horse I honestly have no idea. I have no memory of it. I do remember that I didn't fall off, we didn't crash and I was very relieved when it was over. My legs were a bit shaky when I dismounted.

Being happy to stop when a rider asks is such a basic thing to teach a horse. But it is amazing how many horses can have badly working brakes, hard mouths or need strong bits, or even worse, no brakes installed at all. I love riding well trained horses. That's probably the reason I believe in training and preparing horses well so they can cope with whatever life might throw at them. I didn't want to ride many more bolting horses. I'm very proud to be a coward at heart because touch-wood it keeps me out of hospital.

****

The next step with Ozzie was to install some good working brakes. To do this, I was going to teach him the basics while I was on the ground. The plan would be that when I did finally get into the saddle, the brakes would have been tested and would work nicely. Teaching a horse to stop lightly is actually quite easy. All you need is a halter and ideally a twelve foot lead rope.

You stand in front of your horse, holding the middle of the rope. There is a fair bit of slack in the rope between your hand and your horse's halter. Gently, with the hand holding the rope, you move your hand slowly from side to side, in front of your horse's nose. The rope shouldn't really move at all. You are now asking your horse very politely to take a step backwards.

If you've never done this before with your horse, he'll just stand there looking at you, probably half asleep. That's fine and indeed very normal. If your horse has done this a lot before, he'll probably now step backwards with one foot. If he does this, stop moving your hand, and give him a rub and a rest as a reward. You've just explained to your horse that very light pressure on the lead rope, followed by slight backwards movement by him, results in a release of pressure and a rub and rest.

Now imagine you are in the saddle, at a halt. You lift up the reins slightly, and your horse can feel that very light movement on his halter. 'Aha!' he says, 'I know what that means,' and he takes a small step backwards. Cue more rubs and a rest.

Now imagine you're walking along, still in the saddle. You lift up your reins a little, just enough so your horse can feel you moving the halter around his nose and mouth. 'Aha!' your horse thinks, 'I know what that means'. You are thinking 'slow down'. Your horse is thinking 'reverse'. You now have a very sensitive soft mouthed horse who will slow down or stop from the lightest cue on the reins. That's got to be worth something.

Ozzie's brakes actually got too good at one stage a few months later. When were we riding one day, Ozzie kept stopping unexpectedly. I couldn't figure out what was going on. Dad was about so I called him over.

'Hey Dad. There's something odd going on here. Can you take a look?'

Dad walked over and stood at the fence.

'What's happening?' he asked.

'Every now and again he just stops. Then when I ask him to go on he walks on. It's a bit odd. I can't figure out why he's stopping!'

Dad looked quizzically at me. 'Alright. Well, walk him around and I'll see if I can see anything.'

'Ok'.

I walked him about and sure enough after about half a circuit he stopped. Nicely I may add, and then stood chilled out. It was like he thought it was what I wanted him to do. Very odd. I asked him to walk on again and soon again he did the same thing.

Dad nodded his head. 'I think I see what it is.'

'Really?' I answered. 'What is it?'

'Well,' Dad replied, 'every so often he stretches his head down a little. I think then he must feel a little pressure on the halter and he thinks that's the stop cue. So he stops.'

What a horse. He was so responsive to the lightest pressure on the halter he was managing to give himself the halt cue. It was easy to get around it though, I just walked him on immediately after he stopped and after a few of these he wasn't quite so sensitive. You live and learn!

****

Cinderella is our gorgeous black mare who we bought as a young horse twenty years ago. She had gone through a lot with me. Before I rode her, Dad hunted her for a season or two, and one day a piece of live wire was lying in water and she either felt the current or the wire, and took off at top speed. I was on a lead rein pony at the time so I just stopped where I was and waited for Dad and Cinders to come back from their gallop.

Since then, once every ten years or so when Cinders would accidentally brush a foot against a rope or something else 'wire-like' which was on the ground, she would gallop off in a blind panic. Because it was such a tense and strong reaction I never believed that it was something that I could fix. How can you fix a bolting horse? But because it was an issue that happened so rarely it wasn't something I lost too much sleep over.

Just for fun, I had been going through the rope work and longlining with Cinderella, who at that stage was probably about twenty five years old, and she was being her usual interested and obliging self. The rope work I was doing more to amuse myself and for the two

41

of us to do something fun together, rather than using it towards any type of goal.

It was a warm sunny day during the height of the summer and Cinders and I were up in the long paddock. I had unclipped the two longlines which were now lying on the ground and had taken her saddle off. I gave her a 'well done' rub, and then took off her headcollar. Everything was very calm and relaxed. Cinderella who was now free, took a step away from me and as she put her front foot down again it touched one of the longlines which was lying on the ground.

The split second she realised that her foot had touched (and was still touching) some kind of rope or wire thing on the ground, her whole body froze perfectly still. Her breathing got immediately faster, and her eyes had a panicked look in them. But still she stood there as the panic spread across her face. I guess half of her brain was saying 'gallop away and save yourself' and the other half was saying 'but it's only a rope and Elaine's just spent the last twenty minutes throwing that very rope all around your body and it caused you no pain at all.'

She was literally in two minds.

Because Cinderella was loose in a large paddock, if she wanted to gallop away from the longline that was fine by me. The longline would just stay where it was and she could move away quickly and feel safe again. So I stood there quietly beside her, waiting to see what she would do.

As Cinders stood there, still as a statue and looking very worried while her foot continued to touch the rope, a smile started to spread across my face. I walked over to the opposite end of the longline.

Very slowly and calmly, I picked up the end of the rope, and then started to walk towards Cinders, rolling up the rope as I went. As I passed Cinders I rolled up the piece of rope which was beside her foot, and then with the entire rope under my arm, stood beside her quietly, sighed deeply and gave her a rub.

Pretending that nothing had happened, being the sophisticated horse that she is, she looked over at me as if to say 'yeah, I knew it was fine all along', then continued to walk off slowly on up towards the top of the paddock.

If someone had told me that I could have fixed Cinderella's bolting issue I would have bet a large amount of money on it that I couldn't. It was a good lesson. The other lesson I learned that day was that no matter how old you are, you can always keep learning.

08. New Zealand and Australia.

'Could I have a word when you've got a minute?' My executive producer and I.T. line manager looked at me quizzically.

'Sure', she replied. 'I have a meeting in ten minutes but we can pop into the meeting room now if you like.'

'Great thanks. It will only take a minute'.

I followed her into the meeting room, closed the door behind me and took a deep breath.

'Susan, I've really enjoyed working here for the last three years,' I began hesitantly 'but I've decided to hand in my notice. I'm going travelling to Australia.'

Susan's face looked very surprised. She had no reason to think I was about to depart and had probably assumed I was going to stick around for a few more years. She had been a great boss to work for and I would definitely be sad to leave all my friends. They were a lovely bunch of people.

'What? You're leaving? Really?' Disbelief and astonishment were written plainly across her face. I was fairly good at my job and had been earmarked to progress quickly up through the ranks.

'Yes. I've been here for a while, and I've really enjoyed it, but I'd love to do something different for a while. My new project is starting now so it should be easy to hand it over to another manager without too many issues. I am really sorry to go though it's been great working here.'

Susan looked at me, looked at the ground, and then looked at me again as she tried to think of something to change my mind. 'Is there anything I can do to keep you here? I'm sure we can figure out something.'

I shook my head. 'No thanks. To be honest I really want to go and do something different. I keep hearing of all these amazing stories from friends out in Australia and I reckon if I don't go now I never will.'

Susan sighed and smiled. 'Listen, this was the last thing I expected, but if your heart is set on it that's fine. I'd love to be going with you! We'll sort the work out. When are you leaving?'

'October the third, if that's alright,' I replied, 'and then flying out to Australia two weeks later.'

'Ok', said Susan. 'Well I'm delighted for you but I still can't believe you're off!! You have to promise to let us know how you're getting on.'

'I will do,' I replied. 'You'll be at the top of my email list.'

****

Six weeks later I flew out from a cold wet Dublin airport to Heathrow London, on through Bangkok, and finally arrived at Melbourne International Airport at about 6am with absolutely horrendous jetlag. Like most people in Ireland I'd grown up with Home and Away. For this trip to Australia I had come armed to the teeth with bags of t-shirts, flip-flops, sun tan lotion for the perfect southern hemisphere tan and one week's pre booked beachfront accommodation in the pretty seaside suburb of St. Kilda's.

The day I arrived the weather was beautiful, then it rained solidly for the next two weeks. They didn't tell you that on the television. I found the nearest ski shop, purchased a few woolly fleeces and set about seeing some of the sights of the great Australian continent.

After exploring the city, which included running into half of the people I knew from Ireland, watching little penguins waddle home in the dark, a few dubious karaoke sessions (the new Britney was discovered!), and travelling along the Great Ocean Road, I headed

45

on a fabulously grimy bus trip up through southern Australia. We travelled into the outback and right up to Uluru, with backbreaking hikes through more mountain ranges than I care to remember.

I flew from Alice down to Sydney and then got the worse job in the world mucking out horse manure fulltime in northern Sydney. I quit after three days and soon ended up in a rather hot Brisbane, wondering what I was going to do next. I don't mind working hard but I wanted an enjoyable job. So I surfed the net one night in the local backpackers, and emailed all the riding centres I could find in Australia and New Zealand. I'd said I'd do anything with horses once it wasn't all mucking out.

I got a few 'thanks but no thanks', and then a lady from New Zealand wrote back to say they were looking for someone to help them for the summer season as their normal helper had cancelled at the last minute. I said that I would love to.

So I hopped on a plane to Christchurch, not really having a clue where I was going. Two days later, the Hamner Express bus pulled into a wooden ski lodge in the middle of the mountains and I got off with my huge red bag. I looked a bit lost. A girl about the same age as me with curly blond hair and a huge smile walked over.

'G'day! You must be Elaine!' she said with a gloriously musical New Zealand accent. I had just met a fellow horse person and a soon to be great friend.

Over the next four months at Mt. Lyford I had the best job in the world. The nicest people you could ever hope to meet, glorious weather, magnificent scenery thanks to the incredible Southern Alps, and the most well prepared and well-trained horses I ever had the good fortune to come across.

As a foreigner with an accent that made the locals smile I was a bit of a novelty. They got a few European tourists passing through in camper vans during the summer, but having a 'real' Irish girl living down the road was something else. After about a day I felt like I knew the whole community, or rather, that they knew me.

I used to give riding lessons in top paddock, which was right beside the village road and near the pub. Every now and again random jeeps ('utes' they call them over there) would drive up the hill, slow down when they saw the horses, and then a head would appear out of the window, an arm would wave and an ear splitting roar would be bellowed in my direction.

'G'day Elaine!'

Half the time I hadn't the foggiest who it was but in this part of the country I quickly learned the trick was to wave at everyone.

****

From visiting riding schools and going to the odd lesson here and there, I've met my fair share of dull, mad, strong, lifeless and bored horses. These Kiwi horses were without exception all horses I wanted to sneak back on the Quantas flight to London and bring back home to Ireland. Every one of them was gorgeous.

There were ten in the herd and all of them were characters. Stella was a small cheeky chestnut pony with the kindest heart and the patience of a saint around children. Gemini had a girlfriend called Freya. Basil was my trail horse, a standard bred ex racer and worth his weight in gold. He was the perfect horse in every way. I could have sworn he was Irish. Albie was a beautiful Appaloosa I won rosettes with at the Kaikoura show that year and Cosmo was a huge 16.3 hand Clydesdale cross who was a complete softie and took care of everyone.

I hadn't known anything really about the yard before I arrived, but one thing which struck me as strange was that most of these horses were ridden by clients – tourists, complete beginners, children and locals up and down the mountains and in lessons, in

47

rope halters. No bits and few traditional bridles! I thought it was odd but as it seemed to be working well I didn't worry about it. If a rider was a beginner and was inclined to pull on the reins for balance, I much preferred that this weight wasn't being directed to the horse's mouths via a bit. The horses preferred it too.

For the first month, I continued on as normal, doing lessons, and taking small rides out around the mountains and going for picnics up to Crystal Lake. Then one day, something got me thinking.

****

'Hi Elaine, how's it going?' Kate walked over towards me with a big smile on her face.

'Good thanks Kate,' I replied, 'everything's going really well. The family we took out last week fell in love with Thymie and Cosmo and wanted to bring them home with them to Singapore. It took them nearly an hour to say goodbye to the horses when they were leaving, it was really sweet.'

'Ah Elaine, you're just so cool. I bet they had just the best time.' Kate owned the stables and was a wonderful horsewoman, as was Cathy. She was up to collect one of her horses to bring him back down to their yard in Christchurch. The box was attached to her jeep, with the ramp down.

'I'm just bringing Bird (her horse) back down to Christchurch. We've got a group of four coming for a week of lessons and trekking, so it should be great. Would you mind bringing out Bird's saddle to the ute for me'?

'Sure, no problem,' I replied, and headed back into the tack room. I picked up the saddle, turned around and walked back out towards the jeep. Kate and Bird were walking together ahead of me, and were just a few steps away from the horsebox ramp.

48

Then Kate stopped and pointed into the ramp, and in Bird walked into the horsebox by himself and stood quietly inside it. I nearly fell over with shock! I had never seen anything like it in my life. How or where on earth could I learn how to train a horse to do this?

I started asking lots of questions and over the next two months Kate and Cathy kindly explained the basics to me. By the time I had to say a very sad goodbye and head back to Australia, I had been in contact with Brad Weeks, an amazing Australian horseman, who had agreed to try to train me up in the basics.

****

A few days later I flew into Brisbane and got the train to a place called Caboolture, an hour north of Brisbane city. They had heard that I had been in New Zealand, and were expecting a Kiwi and were well prepared with jokes. They definitely were not expecting someone Irish and my accent was a great hit. The Australians were happy to see I could already ride a bit (I think they had been worried I was a total beginner) so I rode and practiced all day every day, and soon I was certified, happily tired and dusty and full of ways to make good horses great.

I had spent over seven months abroad, most of that time spent on the back of a horse. I was a half Irish, half Australian cowgirl, and what I had learned was more valuable to me than I can describe. I flew back into Shannon airport the following May with my head still full of horses. Leaving work in Dublin had been a bit crazy, but it was completely the right thing to have done.

09. Desensitising

'Morning Ozzie,' I greeted him as I put on his halter. He was putting on a bit more condition which was good. The field was all old pasture so to be honest anything would start getting fat if they were on it. A lot of dairy farms would have reseeded grass instead of old pastures which wouldn't be as suited to horses. My plan that morning was to spend a bit of time getting Ozzie used to ropes and halters to make sure he was completely comfortable around them. A few days before Sean, a neighbour of ours, had come over and I invited him out to see Ozzie. So out he came and presented before him was this skinny nervous looking grey thing.

'He's not too badly put together' Sean said. 'Just trot him up there.'

I took Ozzie for a trot down the passageway and he hopped and leap-frogged his way down and back with his head up as high as it would go.

I don't think Sean was too impressed.

'What age did you say he was again?' he asked me cautiously.

'Five,' I replied. Sean sighed and shook his head in disbelief.

He took another good look at him and reached out his hand to give Ozzie a pat on his shoulder. Ozzie nearly died and took off in a circle at speed.

Sean raised his eyebrow up at me. I could pretty much tell what he was thinking. I had bought some horse alright. We had a lot of work ahead of us.

****

That particular morning was lovely and warm. Starting at Ozzie's near shoulder I rubbed both my hand and the rope on his shoulder for a few seconds. When he stood still I took my hand and the rope away. When he moved, I kept my hand and the rope there. After a while Ozzie figured out that if he stood still I'd stop rubbing him with the rope. Soon enough he was quite happy to stand relaxed as I rubbed both sides with the rope.

'Good horse Ozzie!' He was doing well.

He looked back at me with his best 'I hope you appreciate how patient I am!' look.

The next step was to work on Ozzie's legs and feet. He still had a good few reservations about these areas. At this stage I could touch his legs with a dummy arm while he stood on a loose rein. The next step was to hold a long rope at his shoulder and let it dangle down his leg. He wasn't 100% yet so I didn't want to start bending down near his foot. I was brave but not foolish! His reactions were pretty fast.

Ozzie taught me another good lesson. Do not assume. Just because he would let me touch whatever leg I stood beside, didn't mean he would stand quietly if I accidentally touched his far leg. The first time I did this, he got a shock and jumped away in surprise and looked at me in astonishment.

'What did you do that for?!!! You're supposed to walk right around and stand beside each leg so I know what you're up to!!'

Sometimes horse logic doesn't always match up with human thinking. It did bring home to me though that this horse really had very little handling before I got him. He was more like something straight out of a field.

I threw the rope high around Ozzie's back to get him used to something starting on one side, but then appearing unexpectedly on the other side, like a saddle, numnah, or a person getting on for the first time. I didn't want Ozzie to get a fright when I put my leg across the saddle for the first time. I'm quite good at falling off but I try not to do it too much.

I pretended the rope was the trailing girth and got Ozzie used to it being dragged over his back and then also pretended the rope was a girth I wanted to tie up, so it was dangled from one side. When Ozzie was completely relaxed about it, I reached under his stomach with my nearest hand while still looking at Ozzie's head and ears to see what he thought, and brought the end of the rope under him back to my side, like I would a girth. I held it loosely, to let Ozzie get used to how it felt under his stomach and then let it go again. I wanted him to stand on a loose rein like an old pro without a care in the world. He did pretty well. I made sure only to do things when he was comfortable. Having a loose rein was the key to everything as it meant Ozzie was happy about things too.

After all the rope de-spooking which Ozzie had taken very well it was time for a bit of cowboy roping. It would prepare him for things being high up in the air near him. Imagine playing polocrosse or being at a hunt and someone on a horse reaching over to give you a hot whiskey or some chocolate. You don't want your horse to start panicking and going backwards. You might end up dropping your chocolate!

So I twirled ropes on various sides, over his back and neck and did my best not to hit him. He did his best and was as brave as I could have asked him to be that day. But I still had an awful lot of work ahead of me.

10. Matilda

'Hello, nice to meet you.' I shook Jenny's hand and then turned to her daughter Lisa who was about ten years old and wearing a yellow horsey jumper, jodpurs and boots.

'Hello, you must be Lisa. It's nice to meet you. I'm Elaine.'

I shook Lisa's hand warmly. Another lady walked across towards us and Jenny made the introductions.

'And this is Amy.'

'Hi Amy, it's nice to meet you,' I said smiling and shaking hands.

Amy had emailed me a few days previously to organise a lesson for herself and Lisa. Amy was interested in learning more about horsemanship, and Lisa had a young pony who they had been having a few problems with. The plan was to do a lesson together, introduce some theory and practical moves, and see how the two horses and their owners got on.

Jenny had bought Matilda for Lisa last year as a four year old pony and she had already hinted that things weren't perfect. I like to get an idea of each horse and what the riders want to achieve before every lesson, so I asked Lisa to tell me a little about Matilda.

'Well, she's a bit bold sometimes. Sometimes she rears or she gallops away. If we bring her out, she can be good, but sometimes she just doesn't listen and gets really bold. It scares me a bit. When she stops I make her go on with the whip but then she can start being bold again.'

Jenny threw her eyes up to heaven, and continued. 'I am a bit worried about Lisa not being able to stop Matilda so we've got her in a fairly strong bit at the minute. I don't want her to bolt with Lisa on her.'

53

I completely understood where Jenny was coming from. Bad enough to watch your daughter on a normal pony where anything can go wrong, but watching her on a five year old pony that misbehaved and was quite strong was not nice. I made some notes in my lesson journal as Matilda looked happily out at us from her stable.

'That's great, thanks very much,' I replied. 'We've got a few things to work on then! Would you like to tell me about your horse Amy.'

Amy was in her early twenties, loved horses and wanted to learn more about how to bring them on. She also did a great line in chocolate muffins and biscuits.

'My horse is Mo. She's a nice horse, has been hunted. In the last year she hasn't done too much. She can be a bit spooky and bolts sometimes, and makes faces when I bring over the saddle. I think she might be sore somewhere along her back so I'm going to get the back person out before I ride her.'

I nodded my head.

'That's sounds great Amy,' I agreed. 'If something like that is happening, I would always check to see the horse isn't sore first too. We won't do too much today with her, and see how she goes. A lot of today's lesson will be learning about why we do things, as well as how we do them.'

I duly noted down Amy's horses details. Horses who have been described as spooky or bold or not listening, can sometimes turn out to be really nice once the handler changes a few small things.

We did the groundwork lesson, and the two horses were gorgeous. Amy's horse was happy and relaxed and showed great trust in her owner which was lovely to see.

Matilda was great too – light, sensitive, willing to please and wanting to learn. Matilda already had a place in my heart.

With Matilda, I immediately saw two things which would help Lisa and her work together better. Firstly Matilda was being a normal young horse and was asking Lisa lots of questions. But Lisa wasn't picking up on all of them.

Secondly, we needed to start praising Matilda every time she did something right. It would improve her confidence, make Matilda happier, encourage her to keep trying and hopefully result in more good behaviour.

The simplest way to teach both of these things was for Lisa to lead Matilda around the grass filled paddock we were working in. I showed Lisa how to lead on a loose rein, and how it was her horse's job to walk and stop when Lisa did, without Lisa having to pull on the lead rope at all.

Up to now this had been a problem as Matilda tended to walk into or over people. Both Lisa and Jenny were getting a bit fed up with it. They wanted a mannerly well behaved pony, not a mini tank.

So my plan was for Lisa to teach Matilda that she was in charge, to explain to Matilda that she didn't want her to bump into her any more when leading, to answer all of Matilda's questions, and then to make sure Matilda knew when she did something right and to give her lots of rubs and praise.

I knew I was asking a lot of Lisa who was only young herself, but I could already see that both Amy and Lisa were very clever, patient and talented, and had a lovely way with horses. I had high hopes for both of them, and I was ready to help out if needed.

So Lisa loosened up her lead rope, and started walking down the paddock with Matilda in tow. As she stopped, Matilda immediately stopped too, stuck her head down and started eating grass.

Matilda wasn't being bold. She had just asked a young horse question:

'Lisa, is it ok if I eat this grass here? Cool thanks.'

Then Lisa replied, pulling on the lead rope to get Matilda's head back up.

'Actually Matilda, I'd prefer if you didn't. We're still in the middle of a lesson.'

Up comes Matilda's head. 'Alright so'.

'Well done Lisa,' I said. 'As she's standing there give Matilda a lovely rub and tell her that you really appreciate her being so good.' And so Matilda got a lovely rub from Lisa. Ten seconds later and Matilda's head was down again.

'Lisa, I've found a different piece of grass, completely different to the other bit, so I'm going to eat this ok?' Matilda asked.

Lisa pulled on the rope again to bring Matilda's head up.

'No, sorry Matilda, you can't eat that bit either,' Lisa replied. Matilda thought about it and then checked her watch.

'Lisa, it's nearly two minutes past eleven now so I can eat some grass now, can't I?' Matilda asked, her head descending again.

'Emm, no Matilda, sorry,' Lisa replied, pulling up Matilda's head again.

What was really great was that Lisa wasn't thinking that Matilda was being bold anymore. Instead she was seeing that Matilda was just young, and youngsters ask lots of questions. So instead of getting cross Lisa was being patient and answering each one of Matilda's questions. It's a bit like the endless stream of 'are we there yet' questions from the backseats of cars containing young passengers. They can feel never ending too.

56

In about ten or fifteen minutes, Matilda was starting to run out of questions. We had moved on from leading to hind and forequarter yields, and Matilda was now doing some beautiful lateral work, yielding and sidepassing, and the grass munching was only happening every now and again, not every second as it had been at the start. Matilda looked very happy.

Every time she did something right Lisa made a big fuss of her and you could see Matilda start to grin. Instead of being told she was bold and having whips waved around, her human had started to answer all her questions, so she was learning what they wanted her to do, and every time she did it they gave her a rest and told her she was brilliant. I think Matilda was quite impressed. She was actually a lovely pony. Very clever and honest, and really wanted to learn and do the right thing. It was great how much Lisa and Matilda's understanding and communication had improved in the session.

At the end of the lesson Matilda was led home on a loose rein by Lisa, and after a few quick questions, followed Lisa down the grassy verged lane without Lisa ever having to pull on the lead rope. When Lisa stopped, Matilda automatically stopped. When Lisa walked, Matilda automatically walked along nicely beside her.

Back in the yard, I gave Amy and Lisa a card each and asked them to write down one thing they learned that day. When they had it done, I asked them to read their answer out to me. Lisa began.

'I didn't know that Matilda was asking me all those questions, so now I'm going to work really hard and try to answer all of them for her. I really like telling her she's wonderful.'

'Ah Lisa, that's lovely. You did such a great job today you know. Matilda is really lucky to have such a good owner.' I turned to Amy.

'What did you write Amy?' Amy looked down at her card.

'The same thing really. I didn't realise that horses asked so many questions either and so I'm really going to start explaining lots of things to her and I've really enjoyed today and learned so many other things too. Thank you so much for teaching us.'

When I talk about natural horse people, these two young riders are perfect examples of what I mean. Highly intelligent and quick to pick things up, they wanted the best for their horses, had patience and persistence in buckets, wanted to learn, and had great feel and timing. If your heart is in the right place, everything else will fall into place too.

11. Scary stuff

'Oh my God I'm going to die!'

Ozzie back-peddled in horror as I threw my eyes up to Heaven.

'You're some eejit, Ozzie. Have you really never met a numnah before?'

Ozzie threw me an indignant look which I took to mean 'no.'

A few hours earlier Ozzie had been indulging in his favourite pastime, dead to the world stretched out in his field, eyes closed and only his ribs moving up and down with each sleepy breath.

Ozzie's coat had improved a lot since he arrived and the mud rash had nearly completely disappeared. When he first arrived his rump was noticeably higher than his withers. As he was only five he still has a bit of growing to do yet, and his vertebrae still had to fully mature over the next year or two.

Over the past few days, I had been working on getting Ozzie used to the paraphernalia which he would eventually need to become a confident ridden horse. I had brought Ozzie down to the round pen and while he was standing on a loose rein, I slowly picked up the numnah and held it quietly near me.

Ozzie's whole expression lit up.

'What in this wide earthly world is that foreign object under your arm Elaine?!'

He snorted out loudly through his nose, the debris thankfully missing both myself and the numnah. I'm not a huge fan of buckets of horse snot though I have come into contact with my fair share over the years.

Knowing that I had an extremely curious horse on my hands, I just stood there and slowly the grey nose got closer to the numnah. When it got too close, I took the numnah away and hid it behind my back.

'Hey! What are you doing?! Bring that back!' Ozzie demanded.

Soon the numnah was back and Ozzie was not only sniffing it, but making attempts to nibble it as well. It had passed the Ozzie test.

Once we had got to that stage it was easy enough for Ozzie to stand still as I rubbed his near shoulder with both my hand and the numnah. After he stood still for maybe eight or ten seconds I'd take away the numnah as a reward. Soon I was rubbing it on his neck, back and over his rump. Perfect. Then I went over to the far side and started again from the beginning.

Back on the near side, I started to work on rubbing his back with the numnah, lifting it a tiny bit away from him, and then putting it on his back again. When he stood quietly, I took the numnah away from him completely.

Soon, using this method, Ozzie was happy to stand on a loose rope while I threw the numnah on from the near side and then ten minutes later did the same thing from the offside. I also got him used to standing still while the numnah rested by itself on his back. This was something he'd have to put up with for the next twenty-five years of his life, so I was more than happy to spend ten minutes of my life showing him how to do this properly.

****

The next day I arrived out again, this time with a different numnah and a girth in tow. We went through the 'Oh my God I'm going to die' routine again but now it was much faster and soon Ozzie was trying his best to eat the numnah. Within minutes the numnah had been thrown on from both sides, without any protest from a very relaxed Ozzie.

'You're quite a cool horse Ozzie' I told him.

'I know that!' he replied, throwing his eyes up to heaven.

I thought then I'd see how good he was with a girth. When I showed it to him for the first time, he was interested in it, but was quite suspicious of the noise the buckles made when it moved. When I say suspicious I mean he did not want to stand closer than five feet away from it at any stage.

'Oh Elaine, what the hell is that? It makes a bloody awful noise!'

Cue some snorting, going backwards with both eyes popping out of his head. To show him that the girth was actually more scared of him than he was of the girth, I held it out in front of me and asked him to walk around beside me following the girth.

'That's kind of funny looking. Hang on, it's going away. Hey come back, I wasn't finished with you! Oh cool. When I move it gets scared and goes away. I like this game.'

He was some horse.

After a few minutes of this we stopped and Ozzie got around to a bit of sniffing, as I continued to jangle the buckles. Soon he was trying to nibble it. We were ready for the next stage – rubbing his shoulder with it.

Once Ozzie had decided that it was something which was safe and fun to play with, he was quite cool as I rubbed it around his shoulders, legs, back and rump. Every time he would stand still for a few seconds I would take the girth away and hide it behind my back to give Ozzie a rest. Then it would come back out again. The noise didn't bother him now at all, once he had figured out what it was. It was a good day's work.

****

Ozzie probably had a vague idea about what I was about to do when I caught him the following day. Sure enough, waiting for Ozzie was a new numnah, the same girth, and a saddle without any stirrups. Sure enough, soon he was standing half asleep as the numnah and girths were rubbed and throw all around him from both sides. But what would he think of the saddle?

I picked it up and turned towards Ozzie's head, holding it over my arm. He didn't seem at all perturbed, and after a few sniffs looked as if he might like to start nibbling it. So I thought that was probably the right time to move onto the next stage. I was quite fond of that saddle and Ozzie size teeth imprints wasn't the look I was going for.

On the near side, I rubbed the saddle along Ozzie's shoulder and lower back, and then as much as I could, his upper back area.

Each time he stood still, I took the saddle away and gave him a short rest. After about five minutes, the saddle was resting on his back, and Ozzie looked like he didn't have a care in the world. I can tell you that I was quite excited to see a saddle finally up there, if not yet properly secured and attached to girths, numnahs and stirrups. And I really liked the way that Ozzie was so accepting of it. That acceptance meant everything to me.

I wandered over to his off side with the saddle and after another five minutes Ozzie was happy to let me put it on his back from the off side, as he stood quietly on a loose rope.

I was quite proud of my little horse.

12. Trust and partnership

I'm a fairly regular visitor to various equestrian discussion groups and training forums on the internet. Every so often someone will post a message about wanting tips to develop a better partnership or bond with their horse or pony. My ultimate goal wasn't to own a horse who liked me a lot. If I only wanted that, I would try to do everything Ozzie wanted me to do. I'd let him go whenever he wanted, I'd stop when he wanted to stop, I'd go wherever he wanted to go. This is all probably fine if you own a small dog or cat, but a horse can kill you if you follow them into a dangerous situation.

I wanted Ozzie to enjoy my company but I wanted to be in charge. I wanted to decide where we'd go, what we would do and how we would do it. I wanted Oz to enjoy doing all of this with me and to feel like he was an invaluable part of a team. Basically I wanted to get whatever job I wanted done well, safely and enjoyably. So I didn't want to be a friendly pushover. I wanted to be an inspiring teacher and a reasonable boss who Ozzie admired and knew would keep him safe.

Ozzie had no idea that in order for me to take him out of the stable in Kilkenny, load him into our horsebox and drive him to Tipperary I had to pay money for him. He had not been brought up with the concepts of cheque-books and credit cards. As far as Ozzie was concerned for an unknown reason he now lived on a farm in Tipperary with three other horses, and there was a girl there who came out to play with him most days. She was fairly reasonable which he found a bit strange. Surely she couldn't always be like this?

So Ozzie had no reason to feel under any obligation to me. Because he had put up patiently with all these new training tasks, maybe he thought I actually owed him a few favours.

****

When I was young, I used to go hunting locally during the winter months. I began doing mockhunts on Thady, my little eleven hand pony. The country around where we live is hunted by the Scarteens and it contains some of the biggest, deepest and widest banks, ditches, rivers and dikes you're ever likely to meet in Ireland. It's quite common when moving from one field to the next, to meet a wide and deep water logged dike, followed immediately by a twelve foot ditch covered in trees, bushes and brambles, and then another wide waterlogged dike on the far side leading to the next field.

The children's hunts used to go over the same country. Madness you might think. How could you get an eleven hand pony to jump over a twelve foot ditch? In Ireland horses are bred to jump and Irish ponies will bravely climb whatever is physically too big to jump. They are amongst the greatest jumping machines ever built in the world. As a rider, you only had one job and that was to stay on. Your pony did everything else. He had been doing it for a lot longer than you so it made a lot of sense.

As I grew older I progressed onto Cinderella and I was soon out hunting at the adult meets. Cinders was a natural jumper. Dad had minded her out hunting for the previous two years and now she knew her job very well. She had jumped over more ditches and banks than I had ever dreamed off. Because of this, our roles were simple and straightforward. My job was to stay on as best I could and not get in her way. Cinderella's job was to do the rest.

When I was out hunting, if I asked Cinders to do something and she wasn't happy about it, I wouldn't push her. Instead I'd let her decide to do something different. And she was always right. I finished every single hunt with a clean jacket, and I never fell off once over the years. She was worth her weight in gold, both for her four legs and for her knowledge and experience which I completely trusted.

Having to depend totally on your horse to make decisions to keep both of you safe, really impressed on me how much our horses can give back to us if we let them. This kind of stuff is what's hard to learn in an arena. You really need to get outside and do stuff together. It's not just about telling your horse to do things. It's about working as a team and realising that sometimes your horse knows more than you do. This is a big concept but it's really important. Two heads are better than one if you're doing something as complicated as hunting or crossing country.

If you ask your horse to do something and he doesn't do it, it doesn't always mean he's wrong. You might have been wrong to ask him to do it. That kind of stuff is hard to pick up if you don't experiment and have time by yourselves.

It also made me more open to doing things that my horse wanted me to do. Cinders and I would share ideas and opinions back and forth, and her opinions bore just as much weight as mine did, so I always listened carefully to her.

Going back to Ozzie, I began to wonder what kind of a partnership we had. When I worked in software development teams up in Dublin there was always a great spirit of teamwork and it made for an enjoyable and productive work environment. Would I ever be in a situation where I needed Ozzie to do me a favour and would I ever be in a situation where I could do a favour for him? Funnily enough, I didn't have to wait too long.

I caught Ozzie early one morning and decided to go for a walk with him over to the water trough at the far end of the field to check it was working ok. There were about thirty head of cattle in the field as well, grazing quietly at the far corner of the field. As I started to lead Ozzie over, one of the cattle lifted his head and caught sight of us.

'Jeez lads, you'll never believe what I'm looking at'. This bullock had come up from Cork by the sounds of things.

More bovine heads were raised up.

'What's that then?'

'It's one of those small two leggers and that bossy grey thing moving across the field! I've never seen anything so exciting in my life! Quick, let's all go over and have a look!'

In about five seconds the first bullock had started to gallop exuberantly towards us at top speed. Soon enough an army of cantering bullocks were kicking and bucking their way straight for us. Ozzie and I were walking through the centre of the field, with nowhere to go. This could be interesting I thought.

Having being brought up on a farm, I had a healthy respect for cattle. 99% of the time they would be fine and would back off. But there was always the possibility that you might come up against a wild one who could potentially charge at you. Or at least that was what I was always told when I was younger. When I was down the farm on foot, I'd always stay near the fencing and not wander about too much in the middle of fields that had cattle in them. You just never knew. 'Gored by bullock' wasn't in my list of things to do before I reached thirty.

So I was stuck in an open field with my new green jumpy five year old and thirty head of bovines charging straight for us. I was a bit worried that Ozzie was going to have a bit of a panic attack.

Instead Ozzie was a star. He must have realised that I was a little anxious and just walked on without a care in the world, as if the cattle weren't even there. They crowded around us, jostling each other, braying, constantly moving, stretching their noses towards us and Ozzie could have been mistaken for a trusted old reliable farm horse. He just walked on quietly beside me.

We got over to the water trough about two minutes later. Ozzie stepped towards it, put his head down, splashed his nose around the water for a little while and then took a deep drink. I owed him a big favour.

****

A few days later after a productive training session in the round pen I was leading Ozzie back out through the paddock on his way back to the field. An empty bucket was lying nearby on the ground. As we walked near it, Ozzie started to turn towards it, pulling on the lead rope in my hand.

Some people might see this as 'disrespectful' or as Ozzie being disobedient. But I didn't.

Ozzie was politely asking me for a simple request, one which would make little or no difference to me at all. So I followed him over and soon he was amusing himself rolling the bucket around, nibbling it, picking it up and shaking it from right to left. It was his way of relaxing after spending half an hour concentrating and working hard for me.

****

For most of the initial training Ozzie depended a lot on me. He looked to me for confidence, trust and encouragement, and I did have more of a role as a teacher and supporter. During the early stage he taught me to be more sensitive and subtle. When I started the lateral work though, Ozzie started to teach me even more.

One of the things which I had learned during my time in Australia was how important it was to have a horse whose body was supple, flexible and soft, had a light forehand, and who could respond well to the lightest of seat cues. When I was growing up and going to pony club, things like hindquarter yields, flexion, forequarter yields, leg yielding and sidepassing were things that only advanced riders did. They weren't things that a non-dressage specialist would have to worry too much about at least until the B test approached.

But these were actually basic things that everyone should be able to do. It was only after you could do these, that you had any chance of doing something as challenging as a perfectly balanced, supple, soft circle. It is probably a bit like preparing for a strenuous football match or dance class, you need to warm up your different muscles in your body before you can think of doing something which involves using all of them together. It's the same with horses. If a horse can't soften his ribs on their own, you'll find it very difficult to get those ribs soft while moving around a circle, to say nothing of the other one hundred and one things you're also looking for.

With Ozzie the hindquarter yields had been quite simple. He was a clever horse and with a little time and some soft cues, he had figured out what I wanted him to do, and did it happily.

The forequarters can be a different situation. If a horse is in any way defensive or stubborn or unwilling, they can display this physically by planting their front feet in the ground, bracing their shoulders and raising their head into the air. Moving the shoulders of a braced horse is a lot more difficult than moving the shoulders of a relaxed supple horse. If you're riding a horse who isn't moving very well, has lots of weight on the forward, doesn't like you being in the saddle or has a high head carriage, there's often one obvious thing wrong – his front feet are stuck in the ground. Get the shoulders moving and lots of other things suddenly become easier.

Ozzie wasn't in any way stiff or braced, but instead my normal 'light' cue would send him in a three or four step spin with his forequarters, in the direction I had asked him to go. I'm fairly sensitive and my light cue is pretty light. Unfortunately, I had only wanted one step, not the half a dozen he was offering to me.

I reckon the horse is always right. The horse does whatever is the right thing to do at the time, depending on what choices have been presented.

This little horse was telling me that my 'light' cue had asked him to move his forequarters five steps away from me. And so this is what he did. If I wanted one step, then I would have to give him a cue for just one step, and so that cue would need to be a lot smaller and lighter than the 'five step' cue I had just given him. Ozzie was actually teaching me how to become a better and softer horseperson. From then on, our partnership continued to grow, with me learning as much, if not more from him as he was from me.

****

A few weeks later, Ozzie was loose in the round pen following me about as I walked a figure of eight. As we were heading away from the hedge, a bird jumped out of a tree and Ozzie got a fright. He shied a step or two away from where I was. Then nearly in the same second he took two steps back over to me, and then stood close beside me completely still. It was a cute moment. I gave him a rub and told him I would definitely always protect him against any scary hedge birds.

If I was under pressure, I'd describe a good partnership as a relationship based on mutual appreciation, communication and trust, and one with give and take on both sides. There was a beautiful film I saw a while back in Limerick, set in the Middle East. There were two young boys who had been friends for as long as they could remember. One lad said that if the other asked him to do something really dangerous, he would do it for him. The other boy replied that he knew this but that he would never ask him to do something dangerous like that. With great trust comes great responsibility.

13. Confidence and Curly's one thing.

The sun shone high over the American plains. The old cowboy was sitting on a rock, sharpening his knife as a handful of mid life crisis city slickers, there on a dude ranch holiday, looked on. The three guys were saddle sore, in pain and weary from too many hours in the saddle. They were in total awe of this old cowboy. He looked like he had seen it all. He was also a man of few words. As he sat thinking deeply, knife clenched in his gnarled hand, he suddenly cleared his throat. He lifted his head up slowly along with his knife and looked over towards the three guys, waving the knife threateningly towards them.

'It's all about this one thing.' He said in a low dangerous voice.

The guys frowned at each other in confusion.

The cowboy continued to stare over at them. He put his knife down to their relief and lifted up one solitary finger to underline his point.

'You've just got to know this one thing.' He stabbed his finger in the air to underline his point. 'That's all you need to know.'

The guys looked more puzzled. The bravest of them took a deep breath and replied hesitantly.

'What one thing Curly?'

Curly looked directly at him and sighed deeply. Then his eyes drifted towards the far horizon, and he returned to sharpening his knife again. He said no more for the rest of the evening.

Later that night under the light of a half moon Curly had an unfortunate accident and died unexpectedly. The three city slickers had to bring the cattle home by themselves and they never found out what Curly's 'one thing' was.

The 'one thing' is different for everyone. For me the one big thing in horsemanship is the word 'why'. Just knowing how to do stuff isn't enough.

If you had the 'how', but didn't have the 'why', you could end up with thirty cups of tea beautifully made and rapidly cooling on the kitchen countertop, with no one around to drink any of them. There's not much point in that.

During the course of one of my clinics on horsemanship we would usually cover various topics including leading, handling, personal space and respect, ridden work, softness, responsiveness, communication, teaching methods, behaviour and psychology.

Parts of what I teach would be new to riders. I would hand out the cards at the end and ask people to write down one thing they learned. I had expected that the participants would write down specific moves and practises which they had spent time working on with their horse on that day. But I really wanted my students to figure out Curly's 'one thing' for themselves.

Below are some of their experiences.

'With my youngster, I learnt the most important thing is patience.'

'I've learnt that I've really got to be persistent in establishing my space to teach my horse not to walk over me.'

'Consistency and boundaries. I really need to work on these to end up with a horse who is safe to lead.'

'I do lots of events with my horse, and sometimes I did wonder whether he liked doing them with me, or whether he was just doing them because I asked him to. Today for the first time I can see that my horse enjoys my company. That's a huge thing for me.'

'I started riding two years ago and I can see now how you don't need to use violence to train horses.'

'I never thought I could be a good rider, and so my goals were quite low. But I can see now how I can raise my goals. It's possible for me to achieve more than I had previously ever thought I could.'

What I really liked was that all of these 'big things' the participants had learned straight from their horses.

****

Ozzie had been in Tipperary for four weeks now and we had progressed well. Everything we had done so far had been done in Ozzie's time with Ozzie's agreement, and with a loose rope. I had written out a list of things I wanted Ozzie to be able to do:

1. Basic handling including confidence and respect.

   - Catching
   - Standing still on a loose leadrope
   - Leading well on a loose leadrope
   - Confident around humans
   - Picking up feet while on a loose leadrope

2. Desensitisation.

   - Touching with hands and with a long lead rope
   - Rope desensitisation
   - Walking and backing up quietly over a pole
   - Walking quietly over scary things like a carpet
   - Walking quietly near scary things, like a quad, dog, jeep or plastic bag.
   - Completely comfortable with strange girths, numnahs and saddles.
   - Comfortable around high energy

3. Performance – groundwork preparation for ridden work.

   - Follow the feel of a lead rope.
   - Hindquarter yields
   - Forequarter yields

- Backup and brakes
- Sidepass
- Circling
- Jumping

****

That morning I had gone into Cashel to help investigate some wood boilers. While I was more interested in what colours they came in, an hour later I came away equipped with technical specs detailing the latest advances in low and high canopies, kw output versus room size, comparisons between European and Asian models and the disadvantages of metallic paint on boiler fronts. Thank God horses weren't half as complicated.

It was a beautiful afternoon. Earlier I had seen the four horses stretched out in the grass half asleep enjoying the warm spring weather. According to Met Eireann it had been the warmest day so far that year. I brought Ozzie down to the round pen where I had my saddle without stirrups, numnah and girth. Ozzie was as happy as a duck in water as I threw the girth and numnah all over him, and then put the saddle gently on him from both sides.

I attached the numnah to the saddle, and the girth to the off side of the saddle. Approaching the far side, I put the saddle on Ozzie's back. I walked over to the near side, retrieved the girth, and slowly and gently did it up as Ozzie stood quietly by himself. I walked Ozzie around on a loose rein both directions, and then took off the saddle and Ozzie let out a deep breath of relief. I gave him a rub and told him he was wonderful.

Two minutes later the saddle was back on and Ozzie was loose in the round pen. I asked him to walk and trot in both directions on his own which he did without any fuss. He maintained a nice balanced trot with his head low, allowed his back to round and his hindquarters to move nicely in underneath him. Even with the

73

saddle on his back properly for the first time, he seemed happy and relaxed and he looked like he enjoyed it.

I backed away from him, to ask him to come to me, and he looked at me and walked across the centre of the ring straight up to where I stood for a rub. I was so impressed. He always stopped when I moved away from him, but this was the first time he had actually come the full away over to me. What a cool little horse!

Then I had a brain wave that I'd take a few photos of Ozzie from inside the pen, but Ozzie was determined to stay right beside me. The only photos I got were close-ups of a big slobbery grey nose.

I took off the saddle and the girth trailed over his back and jingled as it passed down his ribs. Ozzie didn't even blink. It was hard to believe that his little horse couldn't be touched four weeks ago.

We had come a long way.

****

To finish up, I did some rope throwing, in traditional Aussie cowboy style - or so I liked to believe - and we did some nice fore and hindquarter yields. A sidepass was attempted on the offside, and Ozzie actually moved all four feet sideways! It was a great first attempt. It wasn't as good on the near side but that was ok. Ozzie tended to do a hindquarter yield and then get stuck, but I quickly asked for a forequarter yield and then when all legs had moved sideways in some way, he got a rub. It was a good start.

The last item on the agenda was probably the most difficult for Ozzie. Picking up his four feet.

For Ozzie, if there was ever anything more complicated than standing still, or more scary than being patted by a human, it was standing still while a human was holding up one of his legs AND was patting it all over.

74

That day Ozzie stood quietly while Dad rubbed his near foreleg all over. At the start when Dad tried to pick it up Ozzie would snatch it away or try to walk forwards or backwards. It didn't work though as we still kept asking him to pick up that foot. 'Time for Plan B,' Ozzie thought.

So Ozzie changed tack and started to put a lot of weight on that leg, so it would be too heavy for Dad to pick up. But Dad bumped his shoulder into Ozzie's shoulder, to get him to transfer more weight to the opposite leg. Ten seconds later after a bit of leg waving, Dad had Ozzie's foot in his hands. He held it there without too many protests for five or six seconds until the split second Ozzie relaxed and then the foot was gently put down. I can tell you it was a great feeling to finally have a foot lifted! It took us four full weeks to get there. He was worse with his front feet, so someone probably had a go with them earlier on but didn't get on that well.

Dad lifted up that near fore again twice and then did the same with the off fore. It was a great ending to the session. I was really pleased with Ozzie as we had asked him some complicated things. And I have to say the saddle looked very well on him!

Starting young horses with gentleness and patience does become addictive. There's just so much potential for success if you can figure out a nice way to work together.

14. Young riders

A while back I had been invited to do a young riders clinic in Grange, Co. Sligo. On Friday evening I drove up northwest from Dublin, and had soon left the rush hour traffic and the suburbs of Lucan and Leixlip behind me. I had been looking forward to this clinic a lot. There's a fair bit of the mischievous child still in me and I really enjoy teaching youngsters. Over the past week I had been working on a schedule for that day, one which would keep twelve young riders challenged, happy and learning lots about ponies.

Teaching young riders is a lot like teaching horses. You need to be patient, funny, encouraging, understanding and most importantly, keep them thinking and have lots of fun. The day would include everything from looking at life from a pony's perspective, working on basic groundwork, fixing pony problems, learning about the most important work with ponies and developing their horsemanship. All I had to do was pray for fine weather.

When I arrived up in Sligo I had a few minutes to arrange some poles in the arena before the first students started to arrive. There was a good mixture of ages from about six to thirteen years and various abilities, and it was great to have a nice mixture of boys and girls.

I shook hands with the children and parents, and soon I saw one parent making her way over to me. Hiding behind her was a shy looking young boy.

'Hello, I'm Joan, Tom's mother.'

'Hello,' I said shaking her hand, 'I'm Elaine. It's nice to meet you.' I peered behind Joan to where Tom stood.

'Hello Tom, how are you?' He looked up at me with big blue solemn eyes.

76

'He's a bit shy,' Joan said. 'He's been off school all this week sick, but there was no way he was going to miss today. He lives for ponies.'

Tom looked up to see what I thought of that statement. I smiled back at him.

'That's great. We'll make sure you have lots of fun Tom!' I turned back to Joan.

'Thanks very much Joan, I'll take good care of him. You're more than welcome to watch if you like. We'll be starting in a few minutes and we should be finished up then at about 4.30 or 5pm.'

'That's great. I have a few things to do in town so once he's settled I'll head out and then be back before you finish.'

****

Once everyone had arrived, we set up camp in the tack room and started off discussing what makes teachers good or bad. I had divided the group into four teams of different ages, so they had to work together to come up with some ideas. I like the idea of mixing ages as the younger ones tend to look up to the older children who can help them and the older children grow in confidence and authority with their new responsibilities.

'Ok. Everyone ready?' I asked the group.

After a few last minutes scribbling each team had a list in front of them. I had asked them to think about all the teachers they had – not just riding teachers – maybe teachers in their school as well. Which ones were good and which were bad, and why?

I got a few very good answers like patience, the ability to listen, good knowledge, sense of humour, being understanding and supportive, and then one of the older girls who was reading her team's list started to grin.

77

'We have one more 'good teacher' one as well, miss.'

'OK,' I smiled suspiciously, 'go ahead.'

She looked at the rest in her group and they all started to giggle.

'Good makeup. It's no good if they're ugly!' The whole room cracked up. Little Tom, God bless him was giggling along with the best of them. I always learn something from these clinics! After a good few more giggles, I gave them their jobs for the day – to become good teachers and teach their ponies some new things.

We put on our coats and headed out into the arena for some practise. They led real ponies and 'human' ponies around on a loose lead rope, with lots of rubs and praise when their ponies did well. Half way through one little fella about six years old came over.

'Elaine,' he said, 'are you going to be here every Saturday?' He looked up at me with interest.

'I'm not too sure,' I replied, thinking of Ozzie waiting patiently for me four hours away in Tipperary. 'Would you like to do this every weekend?' I asked him.

'Yes' he said with a serious face on him, and then headed off.

During the morning, a little girl came over to me. Her name was Kate and she was one of the smaller young riders that day. She looked up at me with a worried expression.

'Teacher' she said politely.

'Hello,' I replied, 'are you ok?'

'One of the boys said I was six.' She didn't look too impressed at all. I took in the situation quickly, and from her height guessed her rough age and added on a little.

'Six years old?' I said. 'No, I'd have definitely said that you were at least eight and a half.'

She looked at me solemnly. 'Yes. I'm seven years old.'

Yes,' I agreed, 'you definitely look a little older than six. Don't mind the boys.'

Satisfied that the world had been put to right, she toddled off back to her team who were currently half way through the pony relay race. She did a very nice job when it was her turn.

The year before I had made a 'young rider's cd-rom' and so during lunch everyone got a chance to play the cd-rom. They all got quite competitive with the quizzes. During lunchtime to encourage them to learn and ask questions, everyone who asked me a pony question got a surprise. It had seemed like a good idea but I soon found myself surrounded by what seemed to be hundreds of curious students with lots of questions!

Very soon pony magnets, pony stickers, pony postcards and pony pictures were being distributed in all directions. The older girls kept the room entertained as well and little Tom was sitting in the middle of everyone, eating his sandwich quietly and chuckling happily to himself for the whole hour at the antics of the older girls.

After lunch we came up with some pony problems and soon the students were pretending to telephone each other with fictional pony problems.

'Brrrrrrring, brrrrring.' Pause. 'Brrrring, brrrrring.'

The other student at the end of the virtual telephone started to giggle, and picked up their invisible phone.

'Hello? How can I help you?'

'Hello, I have a pony and he keeps bucking, what will I do?' the first student asked.

'OK, your pony is bucking. Does he have a sore back?' the second student enquired matter of factly.

'Eerrmmm, I don't know.'

'Have you got him checked by the vet yet?'

'No…..'

'Ok, well you'll need to do that first as he might be sore. Is his tack hurting him?'

'Eeem, I'm not too sure…'

'Ok, well you'll need to look at your saddle and see if it is hurting him. And look at his teeth too. He might need to go to the dentist.'

Student two looked over at me.

'Do ponies go to the same dentist that I do?' I tried hard to keep a straight face.

'Emmm no,' I replied, 'they go to special horse dentists.'

'OK' said student number two, 'then you might need to get a special horse dentist to check him. He might need a filling or something. Do you give your pony a lot of oats?'

'No. Just one big bucket every day.'

'Ok,' said the student two, 'if he's already quite fat you might be giving him too much food. I'm not allowed to drink too much Coke as my Mum says it makes me go hyper. Your pony might be going hyper too.'

'That's great. I'll do all those things then' said student number one 'thanks very much.'

'No problem. Good luck now.'

I wasn't the only one in stitches, but it was incredible to see an eight year old giving very sensible and valuable advice on pony problems to a seven year old.

The 'virtual' telephone was a great hit and soon all types of problems and solutions were being discussed by everyone. The young students were going far beyond what I had thought possible in a single day.

The highlight of the day was an obstacle course to be judged solely on horsemanship. I divided the students into two teams and they were instructed that each time they saw one of their team members show good horsemanship or good teaching abilities, like being patient, giving their pony a rub after they did something good, or rewarding a try, they had to clap their hands in appreciation.

Each team had two ponies. The first two were very well behaved and a good way to start, and then the second two were more difficult – one was a three year old and the other a beautiful but a slightly pushy coloured pony, both of which would be good challenges for the young trainers. All I can say is that they blew me away.

Because the competition was judged solely on horsemanship and teaching ability, they discovered that trying to do things quickly isn't important – how well you do what you do is the most important thing.

They worked really well with the first two quiet ponies, leading on loose reins, going through L's, bending poles and spiral poles, and also training their ponies to walk over a black plastic sheet. When the next two ponies came out, both started off being a little more challenging – the young pony was a little excited and the coloured pony tended to go where he wanted to, rather than where his leader wanted him to. So the challenge for the students was to use all of the characteristics of a good teacher, and to get the best they could out of these two more difficult ponies.

By the time the six students on Team Unicorn had finished with the sensitive three year old pony he was being led happily on a loose rope, looking very relaxed and well behaved, and walked straight over the black plastic sheet.

Team Horseshoe had also done really well – their difficult bargey pony was now also walking on a loose rein, leading a lot better and not walking ahead half as much anymore. All this would be a great achievement for any trainer, but to see young riders who had only a few years experience with ponies, being able to work so well and with so much empathy with ponies they'd never met before would just open your eyes.

Later that afternoon we had prize-giving. Everyone had won special Irish Horsemanship rosettes for excellence in horsemanship and were given 'Gentle Horsemanship' cd-roms to work through as homework.

After prize-giving I stayed perched on my pink teachers bucket and said that if anyone wanted to ask me any questions about horses or ponies that I would be delighted to answer them. About half of the students headed back out to the stables to meet up with their parents, and the other half hung back in the room, asking and listening to the questions, which ranged from what type of a pony I thought they should get, to what age I was when I started teaching and how to load tricky ponies into horseboxes.

After about five or six minutes, most of the young riders had filtered outside and only Kate was left. She stood in front of me with her arms folded, looking down at me at my position on the pink bucket.

'Teacher,' she said 'what kind of pony would be best for me?'

I had presumed that because she was the only one left, this would be a quick question, and then she'd be off. Twenty minutes later the two of us were deep in conversation about all things pony. At seven years old she was completely happy on her own, talking to the teacher about all her pony questions. Every time I'd give her an answer or ask her a question in return, she'd think over it very carefully and come back with another good question or answer. It was surreal to think she was only seven. She was determined to learn and completely happy in my company talking ponies. If she thought this much about everything, she would be a brilliant horseperson when she grew up. Soon one of the other students came back up with instructions that we had to go down to the yard for a photo shoot, but if not I reckon we'd still be up there now talking horses.

Having students that learn so much in such a short period of time is one of the most rewarding aspects of teaching.

Give a person a fish and you feed them for a day. Teach a person how to fish and you feed them for a lifetime.

****

A few months later I was back on the road to Sligo. There had been a waiting list in operation for the first clinic so we had decided to arrange a second young rider's clinic. When I arrived up I had a chat with Una the yard owner and she remarked that a good few of the young riders from the first clinic now came to their lessons early, and if the arena was free they would take a pony and practise stopping, leading, rubbing, backing up and being a good teacher for ten or fifteen minutes before their proper lesson. Una was brilliant to let them do this. I started to get an inkling that the first day I had taught them had actually started something.

During the afternoon of the second clinic Una's daughter and her friend, both of whom had been at the first clinic, were in top form and delighted to see me again.

'Hi Elaine,' they smiled. 'What are you going to be doing this afternoon?'

'Hello you two!' I replied warmly. They were dotes. 'How are you? This afternoon we are going to solve pony problems and then set up the championship course.'

'Oh cool,' they grinned up at me. 'Will everyone be getting prizes again like the last time? Can we do it again? Pleeeeeeeaaaaaseee?' they pleaded.

'Sssshhsssh! don't tell everyone they are getting a prize, it's supposed to be a surprise!'

'OK Elaine. Can we join in for the afternoon? Pleaeeeaaassse.'

What could I say? The best thing about being a teacher is having students who want to learn.

'Sure. You can sit in if you're quiet, and watch the competition later on. How about that?'

'Grand,' they replied. 'Will you be getting them all to ring up with pony problems like the last time? We can help out because we remember all the answers. Check their teeth and saddle if they are bucking or bolting, call the vet if they're sick, remember to be patient and kind if you're teaching them, give them a rest when they're being good, all that stuff.'

I was very impressed. 'You remembered all the stuff we did six months ago?'

'Of course,' they grinned in reply. As if there was no reason in the world they shouldn't have remembered the itinerary, lessons and discussions of half a year ago nearly verbatim. I was amazed.

Later on, Una and I were chatting again with a few parents.

'You know,' said Una. 'I've really noticed a change in the kids who did the first course, in their riding.'

'Really?' I replied curiously. I hadn't done any riding with any of them as I wanted to focus on getting them thinking and working on the basics of handling first.

'Yes. When they're riding they make a point of thanking their pony a lot more and rewarding the pony when he's done something right.'

Months on and these young riders were thinking like true horse trainers both in and out of the saddle. It just showed how important it is to teach horsemanship to children. You end up with really good horse people who can see life from their pony's perspective.

15. A plastic bag and the great tree moving adventure.

'Morning Ozzie,' I said as I rubbed his nose.

'Morning Elaine, bloody hell it's early!' he muttered back, not hugely impressed.

On Easter Saturday I was out early to Ozzie as I planned to drive down to Wexford early that morning for the Easter holiday weekend. The day had begun with a frosty start as it had been quite cold overnight, and the sun gleamed off the drops of dew resting on the carpet of grass as I walked down the path to the field. The four horses were enjoying the early morning warmth munching happily on grass together. Dad was out as well and picked up Ozzie's feet as I held him. It was our third day of doing this, and Ozzie did it well without too many arguments. He was slowly getting better.

'Are you bringing your windsurfing gear down to Wexford?' I enquired as Dad cleaned out Ozzie's near fore.

'Yeah,' he replied. 'There's a bit of wind forecast so I might get out to Our Lady's Island.'

Ozzie sighed deeply as only a long suffering grey horse can. It had taken six full weeks to get to be able to pick out his feet like this. I reckon that was some kind of record.

I put on the saddle without any bother, then asked Ozzie to trot around in a circle. He took off at a burst and bucked his way around like a lunatic. Thanks be to God I wasn't on board as he really went for it. 'Crap,' I thought. 'What's gone wrong now?' I asked him to stop and then walked up beside him to check the saddle. The girth was about one hole looser than I'd normally have it. Surely this reaction wasn't caused by a 'slightly' loose girth? I put it up another hole and scratched my head. Then I asked Ozzie to go out and trot again. Not a bother. He was a funny horse.

Dad headed off and back out in the round pen Ozzie and I did some circling on the walk on both reins looking for softness and bend, and then worked a little on the yields and sidepassing, none of which were perfect, but were improving.

In preparation for getting into the saddle I asked Ozzie to back up with the lead rope positioned at his withers, instead of having me stand in front of him. When I raised the rope a little above his withers, as the cues were very similar, low and behold Ozzie took a step backwards. Bingo.

Ozzie was still a little nervous of ropes around his head and ears so I asked him to turn his head around towards me, and spent a few minutes rubbing all over the lower part of his head with the end of the rope.

While I had been working with Ozzie in the round pen, Dad had driven up from the farm in the tractor, past the paddocks and up to the house.

'Holy cow Elaine what's that?!'

Ozzie stood there perfectly behaved with his nostrils flared out in astonishment.

'That's Dad on the tractor Ozzie. Come on, back to business mister.' We went back to work.

After a few minutes, the tractor appeared out in our front garden, and Ozzie was enthralled.

'Oh my word, it's back again, I think it's going to eat your house!'

I was interested myself as it's not often the tractor is deployed in our garden. Ozzie and I took a break to watch the proceedings.

I took off Ozzie's halter so he could wander away and eat if he wanted to. He had a different plan.

'I'm going to stay right here beside you Elaine. Just to make sure you're alright with this tractor thing. Don't want you to get scared or anything.' I shook my head and smiled at him.

Soon the top of a tall silver birch tree in our garden began to tilt sideways. The tractor at this stage was hidden behind the hedge which winds its way up the driveway, blocking our view. Ozzie's eyes grew wider as he stood beside me. Moving trees. That's quite unusual.

Three minutes later and the tractor had reappeared with a big tree in its front loader. Over the stud fencing it was carried and then the loader's teeth opened and it fell to the ground. The tree was then unceremoniously dumped into the paddock which Ozzie and I were standing in. Ozzie stood happily beside me watching all of this, with big horsey breaths on my neck.

'Wow, this is brilliant Elaine. I never knew trees could do that.' Ozzie was impressed.

Soon two trees were lying in the paddock and then out came the tractor from the back yard, trundling its way down the paddock and both trees were duly dispatched elsewhere down the farm.

After all that excitement it was back to a bit of work, so I put the halter back on and out came a plastic bag. I held the bag a good bit away from Ozzie and shook it a bit so he'd get used to the noise.

'Goodness Elaine, what's that? It moves and it's awfully noisy.'

After a minute or two of concentrating and thinking, the grey nose started to inch its way towards the plastic bag.

I stood there letting Ozzie do all of the work, and soon enough a front foot had also followed in the same direction. Ozzie now had his whole neck and head stretched out to investigate the strange white rustling thing.

He sniffed it lightly and then moved away quickly when his breath made it crinkle suddenly. It was alive!!

I let him rest and think about it and gave him a rub. A minute later and the grey nose was over again beside the bag and this time he blew harder through his nose. The bag made a good rustling sound as the air rushed over it and Ozzie jumped back a step again, his eyes open in surprise. I was chuckling to myself. This was better than reality television.

Ozzie got over his fright and soon again the grey nose was back near the plastic bag. A few more big sniffs, and a few more startled steps backwards, and Ozzie started to think about nibbling it. The noise wasn't an issue anymore.

Now that Ozzie understood what the plastic bag did, it was just another toy to play with. I started to rub his near shoulder with it for a few seconds. If he stood still I took it away and hid it behind my back. In a pretty short space of time I was able to rub his shoulders and back with it on both sides.

As Ozzie was so relaxed about everything, I attached it to the end of a stick, and did the same thing, moving the stick near him and then away from him, as if the plastic bag was flying in the wind. A few days of this, and Ozzie would not bat an eyelid as the plastic bag was rubbed all over him, and was 'blown' all around his body.

It was time to head down to Wexford. The next day was Easter Sunday and Ozzie had a very well earned day off.

16. A visit to England

I'd heard there were some good trainers holding clinics in England, so I had booked myself onto a flight across the Irish sea one weekend. At the ungodly hour of five am I dragged my sleeping body out of bed in order to catch an early morning Ryanair plane out of the bowels of Dublin airport. Pier D Gate 79 is best avoided if at all possible. I was heading to Bournemouth airport, which I reckoned was the dinkiest airport ever. Basically it's a lot like Strandhill airport but without the flying hairdryers. There was no one on passport control in Bournemouth so I walked through one empty room with about six chairs and then found myself suddenly deposited in the car park at the front of the airport. The sun was out so it was quite nice.

I picked up my hire car, a cool blue ford fiesta, started out the right way then forgot to turn off for the clinic and ended up in Christchurch. I've been in Christchurch in both hemispheres now so that was quite cool.

A quick U-turn later and I was on the right dual-carriage way going the wrong way, so one more about-turn and I was on track towards Romsey. As I drove I noticed a few fairly big fields with some ponies in them, and it was only later I clocked that it was actually the New Forest area... I probably need to improve my geography.

There was a nice mixture of horses at this clinic. One particular horse was having issues with the trot. When asked to trot by its rider, it would belt off in a really really fast trot, nearly out of control. The rider would then do a handbrake turn in a small circle, and get the horse back to a walk again. Then the rider would ask the horse to trot again, the horse would take off in a ferocious trot, the rider would do a handbrake turn and go back to walk again. And so it continued like this for a while as the trainer and one hundred and fifty spectators watched on. I have so much respect for people who ride at these events because it can't be easy to have such a big audience watching your training sessions.

The issue was to figure out what could be done with this horse, to end up with a nice balanced normal trot? At the minute, based on what the rider and the horse were doing, they were going from a very fast trot to a normal walk. Then back to a very fast trot and then again to a normal walk. This was all fine but the rider was getting no nearer to a normal trot, so they needed to change their plan to something else.

So the rider was asked to go from walk to trot again. When the horse started to take off in trot, they were asked to turn a circle straightaway as before, but to try to stay in trot and not go back to walk if they could. The idea was that when the horse did a crazy trot he had to work in circles which are hard work for a horse. Then when the horse eventually decided to slow down the trot himself, he would be rewarded by the rider by being allowed to trot on a straight line, which is less work for a horse.

Time to see if this would work.

The horse was asked to trot, so he took off in a mad trot. The rider let the horse do about five or six steps of this mad trot before she turned him, so by this stage the horse had got himself really wound up and did a buck. The rider then did the most elegant dismount I've ever seen, landing perfectly on her feet beside her horse. She achieved this by holding onto the mane the whole time so her head stayed upright. She got back up again.

'Right, what happened there was that you didn't turn the horse quickly enough,' the trainer said. 'I'll help you out. When I see the horse start to tighten and rush I'll shout 'NOW'. When I shout 'now' I want you to turn this horse immediately.'

The rider nodded. 'Ok, I'll do that'.

She rode to the outside of the arena, and then started to trot along the far side. Half a stride of trot later everyone heard a 'NOW' over the PA system. Rider turned horse in a small circle keeping him trotting. As she kept him on the circle, the horse started to slow his trot down to something more normal. After two circles she straightened him out again and let him trot normally. Two strides later there was another 'NOW' over the PA system. The horse had started to tighten and speed up again so the rider straight away started to circle the horse in trot until he slowed down his trot. Back to riding in a straight line, and then another two seconds later there was another 'NOW' over the loud speakers.

This went on for about ten minutes. At the start we had no steps of normal trot. At the end we had half an arena of normal trot before the horse started to tighten up. It was funny, about half way through this, when the horse realised that every time it got faster it was being asked to turn in circles, we got what sounded suspiciously like squeals of frustration out of him. Now I am not one for putting human emotions and feeling on horses, but this little horse was a character!

When she was finished, the rider went down to the far end of the arena and worked a little by herself. About an hour later she came back up for a recap lesson just before lunch.

'How's he going now?' the trainer asked.

'Yes, much better thanks,' the rider replied.

'OK, let's have a look,' the trainer smiled.

Off the rider and horse went on what can only be described as a perfectly normal trot the whole way around the arena. Not one buck, dash, rush forward or squeal.

He behaved like a different horse. This was only on the first day, so on day two and day three they came back and worked on other things, but if you hadn't seen what he had been like on day one, you would never have guessed it, had you only seen day two and day three. Horses learn so quickly sometimes it's scary.

****

Next in was a very interesting horse and owner combination. The horse was a youngster, had been ridden a bit but not recently, and the owner had the horse in longlines walking around the arena. When I say walk though, I really mean was the owner was being partially dragged wherever the horse wanted to go. The horse was whinnying to outside, stopping unexpectedly every now and again, didn't stand still for long, had his nose to floor as an evasion tactic and was completely distracted.

When questioned, the owner said that this horse didn't do any of this at home.

Imagine you've got a scale. You have people who train horses like they are stupid, and use a fair bit of force and pressure to push them around. It's easy for those who see this to think 'gosh, I never want to train my horse like that, in fact I want to do completely the opposite and be as kind and as nice as I can be'. This is a very admirable intention and also brilliant in theory. If I am really nice to my horse, then he'll appreciate this and be really nice in return. It makes sense to us, but it doesn't necessarily work with horses.

After a few minutes of pretty much total confusion in the arena with the horse not paying a blind bit of notice to its owner, and me squirming in my seat watching it all, the trainer asked if he could take over for a few minutes.

On that scale I mentioned, this trainer was in the middle. He was kind and considerate, thoughtful, fair and had a vast knowledge of horses, but he also recognised there was a job to be done. One of the main priorities was to be in a position to keep everyone safe and to do this you need certain boundaries which your horse respects. You can teach these boundaries in a nice way, but it sure does help everyone if they are in place.

So first up was teaching this horse to stop, go, turn right and turn left when asked by a human. He stood to one side and asked the horse to do circles around him on the two lines. The horse was arsey and didn't want to do as he was told. When the horse was halted and then asked to walk on, he did a dash off in trot. We were getting reactions rather than responses. The horse was pulling and fighting, and didn't appreciate being asked politely to do something. There was quite a big leadership issue here. The horse thought he was in charge and behaved accordingly, and his owner had been going along with this. This may be fine until you're out on a hack and you see a truck coming, and when you ask your horse to stop and he starts to jog forwards instead and you end up being run over and badly hurt. There are basic things your horse should do immediately and without question, to ensure your safety. This horse had a bit to learn.

The trainer started to change the rules immediately. When he asked the horse to move on, the horse ignored him. So he immediately asked again more firmly, still nicely but getting the point across. We got a few lovely bucks out the back end as the horse communicated his displeasure at being told what to do. The horse had learned that he was really strong (really bad idea to let your horse learn this) and there was a huge amount of leaning going on into the headcollar he was wearing. After about ten minutes of circling in various gaits on the longlines, and very good leadership from the trainer this horse was arguing much less, had relaxed more, and the go's, stops and turns had much improved. There was no way you could ride him anywhere safely yet but at least he was now on the right track. The ice had been broken, and hopefully we'd see a much different horse the following day after he had digested all this new training over night.

The next day the horse appeared out again. The longlines were on and so the horse was asked to walk on. He duly did, and a nice

94

walk it was too. The horse was turned left and right, stopped, backed up, and walked on again. There was no whinnying to the outside. There were no arguments. The horse looked completely different in his body language and he had accepted the trainer and just calmly did as asked and then got a rest as a reward. If you hadn't seen day one, you would never have believed what this horse had been like as he now looked so 'normal', relaxed and well behaved. This was all achieved in a nice way, and there was now a pretty useful horse standing in front of us who wasn't creating havoc wherever he went. Often if we can train ourselves to be better trainers, you can end up with a transformed horse.

****

As well as working with the horses which needed a few basic things tidied up, it was really nice to see how changing a few small things in ridden work can have a big effect on the horse's way of going.

The next horse had been described as herd-bound, with a rushed walk, and a trot which was described as erratic. Canter didn't happen very often either. When it did it was a bit messy. The horse was being ridden by a confident friend of the horse's owner, and so the plan was to work on all of the above issues over the few days and see where they ended up.

As the horse walked around, the rider was instructed to breathe. It's easy to tense up and use quick and shallow breaths when riding, and maybe when you dismount you might find yourself out of breath. If you're not breathing very well when you ride, there's less oxygen going around all your muscles so they get tense, and your horse can feel all of this, and he will probably get tight too. Instead, if you can do slow deep regular breaths, with exhaling on exertions being really important, this really affects your body and thus your horse's body. I tried this with a horse a few days later who only had a rushed walk and trot, and just by changing the riders breathing, the rushing went away and we got some really nice relaxed rhythmic work from the horse.

For the walk to trot transitions, try not to focus on changing speed. Instead think of it as changing rhythm. Walk is a four beat gait, each foot lands on the ground on its own, so you can think 1-2-3-4, 1-2-3-4, 1-2-3-4. Trot is a two beat gait. Two feet hit the ground at the same time in diagonal pairs, so you can count 1-2, 1-2, 1-2. So, in your head, think of the walk gait when you are walking, and when you want to trot, exhale and think of what the rhythm of 1-2, 1-2, 1-2, feels like. Horses pick up on stuff like this a lot more than what we give them credit for.

The horse looked a bit tight in his shoulders as he trotted around, with a slightly short choppy stride. The trainer asked the rider to relax her shoulders right down. The horse relaxed his shoulders too and the stride got more comfortable and open. As an experiment, the trainer asked the rider to go back to walk, and to curl the toes on one of her feet around the stirrup. The horse promptly looked lame. Small rider changes can have big influences on the horse.

While the rider kept focusing on exactly what she wanted, she played around with the gaits, seeing how fast she could go, and how slow she could go. We nearly got a piaffe at one stage! It really worked to visualise this stuff. If you want a bigger stride, then your horse will need to make bigger steps. So she focused on one of her horse legs, and imagined that leg reaching out further. And it worked. She got more suspension and lift in the trot, and also a slower and bigger trot. The horse and rider duly got a spontaneous round of applause from the whole audience. It was really cool.

At this stage, the trainer asked the rider what she'd like to do next. The walk and trot were looking pretty excellent now, so the rider suspected canter was up next, but she was in two minds about whether she wanted to do it or not!

'Right', said the trainer (reading the situation!) 'Let's work on extended trot'.

'Ok,' the rider smiled back.

During the extended trot, the horse broke into a lovely canter as if it was the easiest thing in the world. They did a few strides and then broke back into an easy trot.

'Jeez, that was alright! Easy huh?!' the trainer smiled over.

'Indeed!' the rider smiled back.

It was a pretty nice way to get both the horse into a really relaxed canter, and also to keep the rider very relaxed about the whole situation. It was pretty impressive teaching right there. I know I harp on a bit about how being a good teacher is really important, but it really can make all the difference.

17. The sore, the great and the grumpy

The arrival of the German discount stores around Ireland had ignited the imaginations of many Irish males. Never had spanners, tools, wrenches, power generators, hedge clippers, chainsaws, bolts, saws, pumps, and various other mechanical and technical equipment been so popular. As the marts become more scarce, these stores contain unlimited treasures for the farmer, DIY wannabe, or any man really. Once a male of the species entered one of these stores you never knew when you would see him again. A friend of mine came up with a theory about men and DIY. There are two types, the ones who can actually do DIY (small minority) and those who think they can do DIY (the rest). You can identify the latter as half way through they start looking for a hammer to finish the job off.

Last year the stores started to sell power generators and chainsaws and people were literally driving around the whole of Ireland from store to store, hoping to get their hands on one of them. An industrious lady was seen exiting one of these stores with a chainsaw under each arm. A few locals were standing nearby. When they saw her their eyebrows raised up simultaneously.

'Wow' said one under his breath. 'She'd be some wife.'

On an overcast Easter Monday, mulling over the past six weeks, I had just spent an hour and a half waiting outside one of these stores. Ozzie had spent six weeks in Tipperary at this stage. In all regards Ozzie had settled in well; the dog was more of a curiosity than a worry, Ozzie was well established as the dominant horse in his herd of two, and he had even got used to the strange black and white beasts that roamed the nearby fields.

That day the plan was to continue the groundwork of the previous days, and then put on the saddle with stirrups, and lie over his back from both sides.

I was hoping to sit up on him properly that Wednesday as well. But sadly the best laid plans don't always work out.

****

First up on the agenda were Ozzie's feet. When we tried to do them in the round pen Ozzie was starting to get quite proficient at backing away rapidly. So for the moment we were doing them in an open stable.

As usual Ozzie was easy to catch. If by chance he didn't stand when I went up to him, I'd slap my jeans and he'd turnaround and face me again and stand still. The three hours I had spent on that cold wet day early on had paid off.

Ozzie was easily led into the yard and then stood quietly in the middle of the stable. As I held him on the same side as we were working on Dad picked out his near fore without incident.

'I think he's getting better alright' I said conversationally. 'I was thinking of trying to lie over his back today.'

'Very good,' Dad replied. 'We'll see what he's like anyway.'

As Dad went to pick up his far fore, Ozzie picked it up quickly and then promptly put it back down straight onto Dad's foot.

Dad did not make a sound. I reckon that could officially be the sign of a true horseman. He gently heaved the offending equine hoof off his foot.

'Bloody hell,' he muttered under his breath.

'Oh no,' I replied frowning, 'are you alright Dad?'

Ozzie stood there unaware that anything had happened.

'Yeah I'm ok. '

Poor Dad. It wasn't a great start to the session! That foot was picked up again without incident, and the hind ones soon followed suit.

After that I led Ozzie out to the round pen, and put the saddle on. I showed him the stirrups and reins, both of which he had initial reservations about and there was a bit of huffing and puffing. After a few minutes he was fine. With the stirrups jangling, I led him around and he was not bothered at all by the saddle or stirrups. Now came the exciting part!

I asked Ozzie for a little lateral flexion, so his head was turned around a little to the side where I was. The idea for this is if a horse's head and neck are turned, the horse's vertebrae rounds like a semi circle and it's physically more difficult to buck. So it's useful when getting up for the first time on a youngster. With the best will in the world there are no guarantees with horses.

While standing beside Ozzie on the near side, I shortened the rein in my left hand to turn his head around to me and held a little mane. Then I spent about five minutes, pulling the saddle over, putting a bit of weight on it, and eventually putting a foot in the stirrup, standing up in the stirrup and then laying over the saddle, rubbing his far side so he'd get used to me starting on one side and appearing on the other. He stood like a rock. I repeated this on the off side and he was great. It was great to finally be nearly on!!

After this achievement we worked on some groundwork. Hindquarters yields I would need once I was officially in the saddle. I threw the rope over and around his head while his head was down, which he was getting much better at, and moved him backwards from light pressure of my fingers on his nose.

****

'Frank. How are you?'

That evening, our friend Frank had arrived over to discuss the new chainsaw Dad had bought in one of the German stores. It was apparently performing very well on hedges all over South Tipperary.

Frank looked at me and grinned. 'I'm fine thank you. How's yer horse? I came over to see how you are getting on!'

'He's grand actually,' I smiled back. Do you want to come out and see what you think?'

We headed out and I caught Ozzie, led him around with a slack rope, threw ropes all around him, waved plastic bags and sticks everywhere and did a few hind and forequarter yields and light backups.

'Gosh, Elaine, what did you do to him? Sure he's like an old horse! That sideways stuff is very advanced for a green horse. I'm amazed. You've done a great job.'

The best part of all of that was being able to walk straight up to Ozzie and catch him in a twenty acre field with an unknown human also in the field. But our good run was coming to an end.

I asked Ozzie for a sidepass which we were still working on. I put some light pressure on the girth area for ten or fifteen seconds while Ozzie stood rock still.

'Elaine, listen I've had enough now. We've had a lesson already today and I don't like being pulled out to do more when its eight thirty in the evening and I have all this grass to eat.'

Ozzie then performed an unscheduled hind leg cow kick in my direction as a general sign of protest.

I wasn't impressed and asked Ozzie for a backup immediately. I did a few sidepasses on both sides, and then finished up with a rub.

My theory is that anyone can have a grumpy day, but you always need to respect who you are with and keep them safe. Being grumpy will not achieve anything. Ozzie got a hug and was left back to his own devices.

18. Loading a racehorse

'Hello, can I speak to Elaine please?' the voice on the other end of the line enquired.

'Hi, this is Elaine.' I didn't recognise the caller.

'Hello, I wonder can you help me? I have a horse which won't go into a horsebox.' He sounded a bit worried.

'Oh, ok,' I replied. 'Can you tell me a little bit more?'

The caller was a man from Co. Clare and the owner of a promising young racehorse. Since the horse had come back from a racing yard she was now impossible to get anywhere near a horsebox, never mind into it. He had been advised to put the horse in a chiffney but didn't feel comfortable doing that. He needed help.

'Ok. I'm heading up to Dublin for two weeks the day after tomorrow, but if it suits I can drive over to you tomorrow. I can't guarantee anything, but I can see what I can do, and try to figure out what the problem is.' Loading huge fit racehorses who don't want to go into horseboxes wouldn't be my favourite job in the world.

'Right. I'll tell you what,' the man replied. 'There's a girl here who thinks she might be able to try, so I'll give her a chance and sure if it doesn't work I'll get back to you.'

'No worries. Best of luck and I hope it works out ok.'

'OK thanks. Bye.'

A few days later, I hadn't heard anything further so I figured they had fixed the problem.

****

Two weeks later I was back in Tipperary and my mobile rang. It turned out to be the man from Clare. The local girl had tried, but they still couldn't get the horse to load. The owner was now quite worried and the horse was rearing and becoming quite dangerous.

The man spoke fondly of the horse, and said that when she had been to the track, she had showed great potential and had a big scopey jump over fences. She was now at the stage where this loading issue was becoming a serious and dangerous problem, and he finished up by saying that he really needed a professional to come down and fix it properly.

****

The next day I drove in the rain from Tipperary through Limerick and on towards the west. As I drove along, my mind began to wander and I thought about the horse I was about to see.

Because this horse had previously been pushed and forced into a horsebox against her will, she wouldn't be straightforward. If she had had one bad experience, it might not take too long to fix the problem, but if she had been taught repeatedly that she was going to be hit and beaten when she was near a box, it was going to take a lot longer. How long it would take to fix the issue would depend on how well she had been trained not to load.

I assumed, based on what I had heard of this horse's behaviour, that she believed the horsebox was not a nice place to be near. I would need to start back at the basics. I would need to help her to realise that the horsebox was actually a nice place. I had to get rid of what she thought (horsebox = pain) and then train her to think something else (horsebox = rest and comfort).

It's a simple thing for a horse to physically walk into a horsebox. But depending on what they've previously been taught, mentally, it can be one of the hardest things you can ask them to do. To get a horse to physically do something like this, it's not her body that you have to train. It's her mind.

First of all I wanted to do some groundwork preparation, before we even got near the horsebox. The horse had to be easy to lead, and good to start and stop on a loose rein. If I couldn't lead her on flat ground, I'd never be able to lead her into a complicated thing like a horsebox with a raised wooden floor, high sides and a roof.

Secondly I wanted a relaxed body, and I wanted to be able to move both her hind legs and her forelegs separately. I wanted to be able to ask her to take a step away from me if I needed to. The last thing I wanted was for her to step over on top of me. I'd need these basics accomplished on the ground first, to make sure we had a good chance of working safely with her in the horsebox.

Thirdly, all sticks and whips, frustration, pressure, stress, and chiffneys would be gone. This was going to be a constructive training session both for me and the horse. Fear, intimidation and violence do not often work as teaching tools. They just cause resentment, insecurity and more violence. And this horse was already far too violent.

Fourthly, I needed to demonstrate to this horse that the horsebox was actually a nice place to be! So we'd have straw on the floor, windows open, and every time she went near the box she would get a rest and a rub. If she stayed outside the box, that was fine, but I'd keep her moving. And if she was brave, and made any positive movement towards the box, I'd reward her – by taking her away from it.

****

The rain began to clear as I travelled west, and I soon saw the stud fencing and stable row behind their house. I parked my car outside their gate. In the yard, I could see five or six people standing

105

chatting. It looked like I had an audience. A man walked towards the gate.

'Hello, Elaine is it?' He seemed a little taken back.

'Yes, nice to meet you. I'll just grab some bandages and a long rope and be with you in a second.'

The owner was polite and friendly, but I don't think I was exactly what he had been expecting. How could a young slip of a girl, standing barely over five feet tall, be able to persuade a tall, race-fit and very aggressive racehorse into a horsebox, when grown men had already tried and failed?

I went around to the boot to get my equipment, and armed with a hard hat, gloves, thick coat, two different halters, a twelve foot lead rope and travel boots, I opened the gate and walked into the yard.

****

I saw her first as she stood in the stable. She was beautiful. A fine intelligent head, bright interested eyes, a glossy coat, and looked to be in wonderful condition. She stood about 16.3 hands high, well put together, was five years old and was really a magnificent thoroughbred.

I rubbed her head and introduced myself and put the smaller of the two halters and twelve foot lead rope on her as she stood quietly. Then I led her out to their small enclosed sand arena and the gate was shut firmly behind me. My audience looked on in anticipation.

My first task was to get her listening to me and to get her to realise that she wouldn't be allowed to walk over me. Initially she was up on her toes, with some rearing, bolting, trying to walk into me, and was difficult to lead.

106

I worked with her for about forty five minutes, being firm but gentle, consistent and persistent, and without any force. Soon she could lead well on a loose rope, had stopped running me over or walking past me when I stopped and was now backing up lightly.

I wanted to get her to move her feet as well to show her that I was in control, so we worked a little on some hindquarter and forequarter yields, sidepassing and circling.

She was also comfortable with me rubbing her head, neck, shoulders and back with my hand, and then doing the same with end of lead rope. I had a training stick there too. I wasn't going to use it as a whip, but I wanted to have something to move her away from me quickly if she decided she was going to move unexpectedly towards me. I didn't fancy getting run over by a racehorse.

To make sure she was happy with this, I rubbed her all over with the training stick, and flicked the rope end of training stick on her back on both sides as she stood quietly with her head low. While she did have an issue with respecting people's personal space, and she wasn't the easiest to lead and was a bit bargy, she did catch on very quickly. Soon she was walking around with me on a loose rein, stopping when I stopped, walking when I walked, without me having to put any pressure on the lead rope at all.

In the first forty-five minutes, the horse had proved herself to be very clever, sensitive, curious, friendly and sociable. The main problem so far, aside from her believing that it was ok to walk over you, was that when she felt under pressure she reared up pretty high.

At this stage I thought we had done well, so I decided that now would be a good time for a rest. Young horses have short attention spans, and this horse had done very well so far. She was led back into her stable to think things over, while we got ready for the next part.

****

As I stood outside the arena while they got the horsebox ready, one of the guys looked at me.

'You're very patient,' he said, conversationally.

'I am,' I replied. Then there was a bit of an odd pause. I'd never been told I was patient before.

As her travelling boots were being put on in the stable, the horsebox was driven into the centre of the sand arena. I checked it all over making sure it was in good condition. It had good flooring, there was nothing sharp to scratch her on, we had lots of straw on the floor, a front window open, and a hay net tied up high in the front. I wanted to make the horsebox as appealing and safe a place for her as I could. If I could make her job easier I would be making my job easier too.

Because I knew this horse had been badly pressured around horseboxes before the last thing I wanted to do was to force her into a battle. She would win hands down anyway. Instead I wanted her to understand that I was firm but fair, and that I'd never use force against her unless she physically threatened me. I also wanted her to realise that she could trust me. I would give her lots of praise and rest every time she did something I asked her to do, to encourage her and prove to her I was on her side.

Two minutes later and we were set to go, with safety equipment on all of us, including a lovely hard hat on my head.

The horse and I walked around near the box on loose rope. She would panic approaching it, sometimes bolting, sometimes rearing. This wasn't normal horse behaviour. This was the behaviour of a horse who has been taught to be afraid.

Her temporary trainers had been so efficient with their methods that as well as training this horse to race, they had also trained her to rear near a horsebox, and to lash out while rearing when she saw a stick of any sort.

I kept a safe distance. While the horse was very threatened and worried when she was approaching the horsebox, she was actually quite happy to step on the ramp and sniff about. She wasn't actually afraid of the box. Like Ozzie she was very clever, sensitive and curious.

As she stood on the ramp sniffing the straw on the floor, I asked her to reverse out by shaking the lead rope. She flew out backwards like a bullet. I could believe that she had won races alright!

She was telling me lots of things. She expected to be hit when she showed interest in the ramp. When I asked her to back off the ramp, she assumed I was going to force her into it, and so she reacted by bolting backwards. What was becoming apparent was that she didn't have a loading problem at all. She had a handling problem.

So I continued to work with her a little. Every time she arrived over at the horsebox, I'd let her sniff the floor, nibble at the grass, or step up onto the ramp, stretch her head up to sniff the roof, whatever she wanted to do. Once she'd do any of these things, I'd then ask her to reverse off the ramp, and move completely away from the horsebox. Instead of me wanting her to go into the horsebox, and the horse wanting to go away from the horsebox, I was making the opposite happen. I wanted her to go away from the horsebox, and she had started to want to go into the horsebox. It's a bit like reverse psychology with humans. The quickest way to get someone to do something is to tell them they can't do it.

In all, I spent about thirty minutes getting her to relax while near the box and on the ramp, and while there was still some rearing approaching the box, when we were at the box, she'd normally step on it and sniff it. As she stood on the ramp I was able to rub her shoulder and back with my hand and the training stick, and she was quite relaxed. I wanted to prove to her that the horsebox was a nice safe place to be. When she wasn't feeling threatened, she was actually very well behaved and stood on the ramp relieved that she had found somewhere where she was safe.

At no time during the session did I pressure her to do anything. Too much pressure at the wrong times had caused this problem. The solution here was to take all of the pressure away and regain her trust. During the session I just made myself busy by keeping us both safe, and letting her investigate things, and rewarding this investigation by moving her away from the box.

She did a few nice spontaneous rears and sometimes also lashed out with a foreleg at my training stick, which again was all previous learned behaviour. I just ignored it. The more people would hit her, the more dangerous she would get.

At the end, she was relaxed standing on the ramp sniffing the ground, so I asked her to back up, and then I walked her over to the fence to chat with her owner, who had been watching everything with interest.

****

'From what I've seen, she's not afraid of the horsebox. She will walk into it without any bother. The problem is she's scared of people hitting her when she's near the horsebox.'

Her owner nodded his head.

'I had hoped to have got a little further with her today,' I continued, 'but as you can see this is a huge issue for her and to fix it is going to take a week or two of time, patience and practise. You'll have to get rid of the whips because they are just making her worse.'

'Aye, so this will take two weeks?' he replied.

'At least,' I said, 'but you'll be fixing it properly. She needs to realise that she will be asked to go into horseboxes, but she will never be forced into them again, which is what caused this issue in the first place. I'd do two or three five minutes sessions with her every day, starting with just walking around near the horsebox calmly. If she does that, tell her she's wonderful and take her away from the box. It's only lots of practise and patience that will prove to her she doesn't have to defend herself anymore. There's no quick fix. It's practise and patience.'

The audience looked on with interest. I reckoned they had been hoping for something a bit more exciting.

As I was chatting away the mare stood beside me on a loose rope. Within a minute or two, the mare's head came down right into my arms, her ears as low as my waist.

She rested her head against me and I drew my arms around both sides her head. She stood there quietly, as gentle as a lamb, breathing slowly and deeply as I rubbed and scratching her head, and massaged around her ears gently. She was such a beautiful sensitive horse, but had just been unlucky. As we stood there, it was as if she was willing me to tell them that all she wanted was a second chance to do the right thing.

'Do they have many good horsemanship trainers in Tipperary?' the owner asked me with a wry smile.

I don't know of many,' I replied truthfully. It was only while thinking about that question in the car on the way home that I realised it might have been a backhanded compliment.

While I started a process that day, it would only work if her owner continued to do the work, slowly and patiently, that I had begun. I still don't really know what he thought of what I had said. What he did next was up to him.

19. Six weeks: in the saddle

A DVD I had ordered a while back from the States had arrived in the post. It was a video of a 'young horse starting' event held in Texas. They had turned a car park right in the centre of this city into horse pens, three round pens and tiered spectator seating, and arranged for three of the most highly regarded American horse trainers to start a young horse - in two and a half hours. Once completed this would be followed by a competition – set work, an obstacle course and freestyle - in which the trainers would compete against each other on their young horses.

The commentator was humorous and lively and watching what each trainer was doing with their young horse was fascinating. I was glued to it, comparing and contrasting it against my own horse.

I'm not a big fan of the 'how much can you do in a short time' approach. But this video showed how important trust and confidence is when training a young horse.

Lack of trust can make a trainer's job difficult, unpredictable and at times dangerous. With trust and confidence established, it's a different situation. When it came to the official judging, the horse who had the most confidence and trust in his trainer displayed the most soft and supple performance. He walked and trotted very relaxed and free, looking like he'd been ridden every day for the last few weeks. He was calm and confident even when walking through strange things and having a straw bale dragged behind him, and was even sidepassing at the end. While the other horses were having the odd difference of opinion with their trainers, this little horse and his rider seemed to be working together.

One of the tasks the trainers had to do was to walk, trot and canter their horse, and marks were assigned for each task. This trainer declined to canter, forfeiting the marks on the grounds that he didn't want to push his horse into doing something he wasn't yet ready for.

Bear in mind that there was a crowd of thousands, a DVD was being filmed, and a prize was at stake – this trainer put his horse first, forfeited the canter marks, and still won the overall prize. He proved in more ways than one that he was both a talented and honourable trainer, with his horse's welfare and confidence at heart. And his horse showed it.

****

Two hours later I dragged myself away from the DVD, caught Ozzie and did some groundwork.

For fun we backed over a pole on the ground, which he did softly. Hindquarter and forequarter yields went well on both sides, as did the sidepass. Backup from a light nose pressure was improving as were his forequarter yields. He had got much lighter in his front end and was moving from a halt to a walk, both right and left, from just raising the rope and pointing towards the direction I wanted him to go. His feet passed without incident, and so last on our agenda for the day was our most exciting one - sitting in the saddle for the first time!

****

I brought Ozzie into the round pen and saddled him up as he stood quietly.

'This is a big day Ozzie!' I informed him solemnly. He stared blankly into the distance with his head low and sighed. It was just a normal day for him.

It was the third day that I had put the saddle and stirrups on, walked and trotted about and leaned over his back at a standstill. I turned his head around to me, and then put my foot in the near

113

stirrup and gently lifted myself slowly into the saddle, being careful not to touch his rump unexpectedly on the way over.

Oh my gosh I was sitting on my horse!!!! What a great view. Ozzie continued to stand still on a loose rein, as I worked hard to contain my excitement and pretended to be completely relaxed.

However I was keeping a very close eye on Ozzie the whole time. Before I had mounted, Ozzie's body had been totally relaxed. Now though, his body had got tense and his ears were pointed directly back at me. He was very focused on what I was doing up there.

'This is very weird Elaine. What are you doing up on my back? There hasn't been anyone on my back for over two months. What are you going to do now? I'm a bit nervous.'

To reassure him everything was ok I sat quietly in the saddle for a few minutes and gently rubbed both sides of his neck, as he looked at me out of one eye and then out of the other. If anyone was watching it probably looked very boring. It was far from boring though I guarantee you!

As we stood still, after a while he started to relax and his ears started to alternate between me, the front, and to the left where he'd seen something in the distance. As I sat there for another few minutes, he relaxed more again. Then I dismounted and gave him a few minutes to think it over.

What a cool little horse!! I can't explain properly the buzz I got from sitting up in that saddle for the first time. Part of the reason it meant so much was that it really had taken six weeks of hard work to get Ozzie to this stage.

Soon I hopped on again, this time from the off side. Again, I kept a close eye on Ozzie all the time I was up in that saddle. My first goal was to make him comfortable and confident with me sitting up there.

After a few minutes more, when he looked pretty relaxed, I asked Ozzie to turn his head around. He did this no bother and then I put my leg behind the girth to ask for a hindquarter yield, which he also did nicely.

Then more rubs at a standstill while he thought about things for a minute or two. Then I repeated the bending on the other side. No problems. Throughout everything Ozzie was very focused on what I did. This was just brilliant!

Before I asked Ozzie to take his first step forward with me in the saddle, I wanted to make sure he had good brakes. So as I sat in the saddle, I lifted my reins up gently. Because of the backing up groundwork we'd done over the last few weeks, once Ozzie felt this light cue, he took a step backwards.

'Oh Ozzie, you are such a brilliant horse!' a smile lit up my face from ear to ear.

With the brakes in place and working, we did a small circle in walk around the round pen, which he did nicely and relaxed with his head at a nice low level. Then we stood still again for a while and I just enjoyed the view through his ears.

Then I got off, gave him a two minute break, and then got back on again. After some more backup, lateral flexion and a walk on the other rein, it was time for a rub, and then a dismount again on the offside.

It was my first day in the saddle!!

I was so happy it was incredible. I floated back to the house on cloud nine.

20. Bertie the gorgeous draft.

Hello,

Bertie's the name and I'm writing for my owner (oh I am the horse...well to be precise a gelding as of today.... I'm not too happy about that either).

I'm a year and a half old, heavy boned cob. Quite a handsome fella really...now I'm not one to brag but that's what she tells me everyday. Thing is my owner is having a tough time for the past while. Well let's just say I think I'm driving her over the edge...but she's not getting it.... she keeps coming back for more. I bite her daily, will not walk on the lead rope (hey a horse must run.....ye horse lovers will understand this.... It's in the blood).

I walk into her space all the time and I know that she hates this because I corner her and bite her knees. I wouldn't let her groom me until she has come up with a cunning plan and grooms me whilst I eat my hay and that works ..... because a man's got to eat. When she tries to do my hooves I bite her on the back..... oh that gets a reaction not as good though when I bite her breast. Well now I am feeling a bit guilty because she is so so so trying to work with me but she needs some help.

She took a day off work yesterday to visit equestrian centres looking for someone to help her. I have never seen her so sad when she returned. She chatted with me as she always does, and the suggestions were 'a good couple of hard slaps will sort him' or and another one suggested a 'whip'. The others offered to take me in for a few weeks and sort me. So that's why I'm writing I don't want to go anywhere you see.... Now she assured me that would not happen because she wants to achieve these things herself with me under guidance. Well, given the way I carried on today as they tried to sedate me it may have been the straw that broke the camel's back. So here I am rooting for her in the hope that perhaps

116

someone can give advice to her.... see it's a communication problem....she does not speak horse and I don't speak English too good....so she needs to learn my language, as you can see I have learned hers!

She is a soft touch really. When I was sick with colic I was only a year old she slept in the stable with me, watching over me...she brought me to hospital and visited me every day, bringing me a bag of my hay and feed so my tummy wouldn't get any further upset and this other time when.....oh oh must go here she comes checking to see I'm okay after my gelding today.....does this lady ever sleep (she has work in the morning but took today off work as well so she could be home with me....and the other two ponies and five dogs)..... please help her..... must go have to hide the laptop under the hay....

Thanks for your time and hooves crossed,

Bertie.

****

I arrived down in Carlow on a warm Friday evening, about a week after I had got Bertie's email.

'Hello, are you Sarah by any chance?'

The lady had been standing by her gate looking like she had been waiting for someone as I drove towards her house entrance.

'Oh yes, great to see you Elaine, just drive straight in.'

I parked my car, put on my best wax jacket and headed out with Sarah to meet Bertie who was in a paddock behind the house.

'He's just around the back here. I can't put him in the big field as I can't catch him,' Sarah explained. Soon enough we had passed the

117

stables, and I was met by the cutest black and white yearling I'd ever seen.

'Oh my God he is so gorgeous!'

Bertie was just adorable with big fluffy feet, a furry coat, friendly face and a white knee. He was the kind of young horse you'd see on those equestrian calendars in the shops every Christmas.

He had been gelded about nine days ago, and since then his biting had become much better.

'How do you catch him when he's out in the paddock?' I asked Sarah.

'If I put some food in his stable, and then open all the gates he's very good at walking straight in himself.'

'Is he ok to handle?' I asked. Sarah nodded.

'Yes, he's quite sociable and friendly, just all of his biting was getting nearly impossible. It's difficult to put a headcollar on him though, and when I lead him he tends to run into me.'

From my perspective, there were a few things we could work on. Sarah would need to be able to catch Bertie easily in the small paddock, as otherwise when he was put out in a bigger field it would be really difficult. Sarah also needed to be able to put the headcollar on without using food. It should be something Bertie accepted and was happy to do without bribery. Thirdly, we needed to be able to lead Bertie safely on a loose rein, and stop him running over the person who was leading him. And lastly, we needed to work on reducing the biting which was going on. This was going to be fun! I love little horses.

****

118

As Bertie was already out in the paddock, I decided that first we'd work on catching. And I wanted him to show me how comfortable he was around people.

At the beginning he'd stand with his tail towards me, looking out over the gate or nibbling at some grass beside the fence. I would whoosh him away, and he'd walk or trot on away from me.

Every so often, he'd turn his head around to me, and the split second he did that, I stopped making noise and walked away from him.

You could see his brain was whirling at top speed.

'Ohh! What did I do there? I just made her go away! Cool.'

We did this a few more times and you could see that Bertie was starting to realise that when he looked at me, I'd move away from him.

A few minutes later he was curious enough that when he looked at me and I started walking backwards away from him, he walked forwards towards me as if he wanted to catch me.

Soon I gave up (!) and stood there quietly, and Bertie walked right up to me and stood beside me. I rubbed his head, shoulder, neck and back as a thank you. He really was lovely.

After a while Bertie walked off again, so I began shooing him away again and soon enough he looked back towards me, and I stopped.

Three minutes later and Bertie had 'caught' me again. We did this a few more times, and he was very comfortable standing beside me while I rubbed him.

Bertie had figured out how the game worked, and was now making me work – instead of turning his whole head around to look at me like he did at the start, he was just glancing at me, to see how in tune I was with him, and to experiment and see how sensitive I really was to his movement.

As the rules of the game meant that any time he looked at me (even a split second glance) I had to move away, he was putting me through my paces and I had to concentrate very hard and be really focused.

This was going very well and soon Bertie was catching me in the paddock quite quickly. While he was standing beside me, I now wanted to see what his tolerance for headcollars was. Seeing as how up to this point this was only done in a stable with a bucket of food, I didn't expect it to be too easy. I was right.

****

I could rub his head and nose with my hand, but when I tried to put the headcollar near his nose, or turn his nose around to me without the headcollar, he'd start slowly walking backwards to avoid it. Which was fair enough.

Catching a horse out in a paddock is difficult, especially if he's not easy to catch in a smaller area. I needed to make this easier for both of us.

I asked Sarah to show me how she gets Bertie into the stable, so once the gates were open Sarah called Bertie. In he came straight from the paddock through the yard and straight into the stable like a professional. Then we took all of the food out of the stable.

****

'What I'm going to work on now for a minute or two is to get Bertie happy to stand still while I rub him, and then ask him to turn his head around to me a little,' I told Sarah.

'I'll start off, and then once you see what I'm doing, I'll get you to do it as well, if that's alright. Before we can put the headcollar on

120

Bertie needs to learn how to stand still when we're near, so we'll start with this first.'

'Perfect, that sounds great Elaine.'

I put my hand on Bertie's nose and asked him gently to bend his neck slightly to me. The split second he turned his neck a fraction, and offered some softness and relaxation and wasn't pulling against my hand, I took my hand away as a reward.

Whenever Bertie argued (walked backwards, walked forwards, lowered his nose, shook his head, turned away from me) I just walked with him, and let him do what he wanted to do, but kept my hand on his nose. It's much easier to put a halter on a horse who is already relaxed and willing, rather than one trying to get away from you.

Now it was Sarah's turn.

'OK, so the idea is that you ask Bertie to gently turn his nose a little towards you by putting your hand where his noseband would lie. If he moves, you have to keep your hand on his nose. If he turns his head a little towards you, you can let go.'

'OK grand,' said Sarah. 'I'll try that.'

Sarah was brilliant. She would ask Bertie to turn his head a little, and soon he would be moving backwards, sideways, and putting his head down really low to get out of doing it.

'Gosh,' Sarah said, 'this is tough work!' Bertie was doing his best to do everything except turn his head.

'Normally when he starts doing this I give up. I see what you mean though about only rewarding him with a rest when he does what I want him to do.'

121

'You're on the right track Sarah,' I said. 'Bertie's just trying to figure things out.'

Soon enough Bertie stood still and turned his head a little around towards Sarah.

Sarah immediately took her hand completely away from his nose.

'Wooohoo fabulous!' I said. Sarah had a big smile on her face.

'That was cool,' she replied. 'He did it for me!' We all had a well deserved short rest.

Sarah and I continued to practise this with Bertie from both sides. The whole time the 'arguments' were getting shorter and less frequent.

Bertie was beginning to learn that when a human put a hand on his nose and asked him to bend his head around a little, the simplest reaction was just to stay relaxed and turn his head around, rather than trying to move away from the human.

If he turned his head around gently and stayed calm, he could 'train' his human to take their hand off his nose. How clever was Bertie?! And Sarah was great too, being persistent when needed, and being patient with Bertie to help him to understand what she was looking for him to do. Together they made a great team.

****

Next I brought out the halter. Putting on a halter is a big task for a little horse.

It's much easier to teach a horse five easy things instead of one difficult thing, so I decided to break down the halter training into some easy steps. Step one and two we'd done already. Bertie was happy for people to stand beside him and rub him, and he was also

122

now much more accepting of people putting a hand on his nose and turning his head around to them.

The next step would be to rub his nose with the halter while his head was turned around.

In about five minutes, both Sarah and I had done this with Bertie on both sides. And the important thing was that we weren't forcing him to accept this – he was standing relaxed without a bother in the world, which for me meant we were doing something right.

Next on the agenda was to slip the headcollar over Bertie's nose, while his head was turned a little. Again, five minutes later and this was done on both sides.

The really important thing here was when we put the headcollar over his nose and he stood still and relaxed, we immediately took the headcollar completely off his nose, and stepped away from him as a reward. Bertie was learning fast.

After this was 100%, then it was nose turn, followed by the halter slipping up over his nose, and the headpiece being put over his head.

When Bertie stood still relaxed, off came the headcollar completely as a reward and we went away. It was like a game. He thought so too and often followed us around the stable when we 'went away'!

By the end of the session I wanted Bertie to think that catching, head turning, putting on the halter and leading, were all fun things to do. If your horse enjoys being caught, he will probably be quite easy to catch.

After about thirty times of putting the headcollar near Bertie, then over his nose, and then completely on him from both sides, he was a lot more accepting and happy with the situation. With some more practise Sarah wouldn't need to use the food bucket to get the headcollar on any more.

****

The final thing we had to do was leading. Up to now I'd say Bertie had bit us or tried to bite us about three times. A lot of his unwanted behaviour had started to go away since he had been gelded. So while there was still the odd nip, it wasn't a big issue any more and other than advise Sarah to push his head away when he was about to nip, I suspected it would sort itself out.

Bertie wasn't used to being led on a lead rope, so I took him back out to the paddock and soon we were starting and stopping on a loose rope.

When he stopped when I did, he got a rub and a rest, and when he walked on after I stopped, he was asked to take a step or two backwards, and then got a rub.

The most important part here was the loose rope – I didn't want to force Bertie to stop by holding him really tightly, because that wouldn't fix the problem. That would just be a band-aid and once I let the rope go the problem would reoccur.

Instead, Bertie could choose to stop with me or keep going. I let him figure out the consequences and he could make his own decisions.

Now it was Sarah's turn. Horses love an inspiring leader who emits confidence and assurance so Sarah's job was to walk like it was a pound a pint in the local pub and it was five minutes to closing time.

At the beginning it was tricky for Sarah to remember about keeping a loose rein, and her hand would move up the rope, but in about ten minutes she was doing really well and Bertie was behaving like a gentleman, stopping and starting when she did, with very little contact on the loose rope.

'That's great Sarah. He's really come on a lot, hasn't he?'

124

'Oh Elaine, this is great. I just feel like I understand him a lot more now.'

'He is a gorgeous horse,' I replied. Bertie looked up at us from under his white eyelashes. He was a cool and very happy little horse.

'You did brilliantly Sarah. He just needs a little patience and persistence, and lots of rest and praise when he gets it right, and he's going to turn out beautifully. I think we'll leave it there for today as he's done a fair bit. I'll give you some homework for him though, and if you have any questions just drop me an email at any stage. I'll look forward to hearing how you get on!'

'He'd been so good today. I'll practise all the things we did and let you know how we get on. Thanks a million for coming down.'

As dusk fell I left Sarah and the gorgeous Bertie, and drove on down towards Carlow town, and then on towards Tipperary.

A few days later there was another familiar looking email in my inbox.

Hi Elaine,

Had to write to give you a quick update....sure Bertie is doing great helping me with his homework. Each time I went into the paddock today he came straight up to me and stood for a rub, and each time I moved away from him he followed beside me keeping out of my bubble. You would think I had an invisible string attached to him. He was great. Wasn't as keen on the exercises in the stable but we got there. I then just spent some time in the stable with him just chilling. Here's the thing though not once did he try and nip me today, he was so chilled today but then so was I. He really was a pleasure to be around today and enjoyable company and I think he may have thought the same about myself...well I'd like to think that anyway.

So things are on the up and up and the times it goes pear shaped as I am sure it will I will hang on to those good moments. Thanks a million for all your help the other day. Through the exercises you showed me, and the understanding of the language of the horse you created, you have instilled a confidence in myself that I can do this....well with a bit of help or ....maybe a lot!!!!. Will keep you posted. Oh by the way, Bertie asked me to give you his carrot that he should have had today. Said he wanted to give it to you as a thank you. Muttering to me as I left that it was nice to have someone (that being you) around that talked sense.... cheek of him eh?. suggesting I don't !!!!

Thanks again,

Sarah and Bertie.

21. Early rides in the saddle

Mention the possibility of warm weather to Irish people and our genetically pale faces light up. In the Mediterranean it was lashing rain but in Ireland we were having three weeks of hot April weather, a sure sign that the weather systems had gone a little haywire. Over the weekend I had been up in Dublin doing some horse clinics so Ozzie had the benefit of two days holidays to sunbathe and to boss Pepsi.

Ozzie and Pepsi had been put back into the paddock, as the cattle had taken up residence in their field. When I went out to catch Ozzie he was really pushing Pepsi about. Pepsi being over thirty and arthritic isn't a good partner for such playful and boisterous activities. After the session I decided they would be separated. Pepsi had done his baby-sitting job perfectly and now he deserved a break from the playful younger horse. Ozzie was going to go out with the cattle.

On the ground, our hindquarter yields, right and left turns and backups were working well. I picked up his four feet and he stood on a loose lead rope in the paddock, which was good progress as well.

I put the saddle on again and then got him to do an easy trot on both reins, then checked the girth again. When I taught at a stables in the Cotswolds, after watching tack being flung on various ponies who weren't that happy about it, I did a tacking up demo one day for the young helpers who worked at the stables part time. The main idea was that all the ponies should be happier after they were tacked up than they had been before. The kids were great and really got into it and the ponies looked a lot happier.

I got up for the second time, on the near side and got off on the far side as Ozzie stood quietly. Like the previous day when I was in the saddle Ozzie was very focused on me, with his ears pointed back

127

listening to me. After a minute or two of standing still he started to relax again.

Ozzie continued to stand quietly as Dad left the round pen. Previously he had been focusing on the person standing nearby, rather than the person on his back. That was understandable as I'd just spent the previous four weeks training him from the ground. Walking, trotting and cantering correctly, with bend, softness, flexion, soft ribs, loose shoulders, engaged hind end and with no weight in my inner hand at all.

I asked him to bend his neck while keeping his feet still, so after a circle of walking he stopped with his head and neck turned around towards me. Then I gave him a rub and loosened the reins so he could stretch out. The idea being that when he did what I wanted he got a nice reward. We repeated it on the other rein. After a few more tries, he was happy just to turn his head around to me either way when he felt the cue, rather than going through the circle walking part of the process. We did some nice hindquarter yields and very light backups.

Sometimes when I worked with Ozzie I didn't always see a lot of progress. Sometimes it actually felt like we were discovering even more things we hadn't done yet. But then sometimes I remembered how far my horse had come. From my new position high up in the saddle I began to imagine the fun things that we would soon be able to do.

****

Our new task for the day was to obtain lateral flexion and then to ride a circle, both right and left, calmly and relaxed with a bend in his body in that direction. Ozzie was cool! At the start it went something like this:

Elaine: *Walk on please Ozzie.*

128

Ozzie: *Ok.*

Ozzie (two strides later): *Right, done that so I'll stop now.*

Elaine: *Actually, could you keep walking Oz?*

Ozzie: *Ok, sure.*

Ozzie (two strides later): *Right, is that it, can I stop now?*

Elaine: *Emmm no, some more walking please Oz. I'll tell you when I want you to stop.*

Ozzie: *Oh ok – shall I just keep on walking then?*

Elaine: *Yes please.*

Ozzie: *Grand.*

A very effective way to ride a circle is just to use your inside rein and inside leg. The other leg and rein you only use if you need to adjust something specifically. The idea is that your inside hand will ask for the horses head and neck to bend in, like the circle he's walking. Your inside leg will push his ribs out, so he'll get that ')' arc in his body.

If you use your outside hand you can make his head turn out (which you don't want) and if you use your outside leg you make his ribs push inwards, which will make his body go in the opposite bend to the circle that he's walking on, which you don't want either. Over in Australia when working in circles in a small round pen, you'd actually just be given the inside rein to use. Sounds strange, but it worked really well.

While my inside hand was working well and Ozzie had nice lateral flexion, what I also needed to work on was soft ribs. So when I put my inside leg on, his ribs were pushed away from my leg, and his side actually wrapped around my leg, achieving that perfect latitudinal arc for moving correctly on a circle. The way I taught him to yield to my leg was through sidepassing on the ground. I needed to teach Ozzie that pressure on his girth area means 'move away from the pressure'.

When we finished we stood quietly together watching the rabbits play. Ozzie was chilled and relaxed, and sitting up there as dusk settled in around us, it felt as if Ozzie was a horse that had been around for a good few years. A comfortable silence had descended around us.

As I sat there, Ozzie reminded me of an old horse – quiet, relaxed, trustworthy, predictable and reliable. A good start in life can dictate to a large extent what kind of life your horse will lead.

****

While Ozzie was confident with me he still was a bit wary of Dad. His previous owner had been a man and I guess that coupled with having spent the last few months with me mainly, he was still a bit unsure of Dad. One day all this changed. Dad was out watching me while I did a bit of groundwork with Ozzie. It was getting pretty warm now so there were awful horseflies buzzing about. Ozzie really hated them. Anyway as I was doing a bit of work, every now and again Ozzie swished his tail or tried to bite the flies as they landed on his body. Dad doesn't like horseflies either, so he began to help out Ozzie by brushing them off if he saw any land on Ozzie. Now Ozzie is no dope. He twigged pretty quickly that Dad was an asset to have around the place. Dad's true technique for dealing with horse flies involved creeping slowly up near them, and then belting them away in the hope of doing as much damage to them as possible.

So this meant walking slowly up beside Ozzie and then whacking whatever ever area the fly had landed on. The horse was absolutely delighted. After a while it got to the point where Dad could walk up to Ozzie anywhere and then give him a good firm swipe on any area of his body, including between his back legs and Oz would not bat an eyelid. That was pretty good for a horse who didn't like being rubbed.

22. Smile and enjoy it!

If you ever watch a great horseperson they never get angry or frustrated. They analyse where the horse is and what issues he's got and then proceed to work calmly on those specific issues. You can do this without knowing heaps as well. Stay calm, figure out the issues, and then go and talk to other people to see if they've ever come across these issues before, and keep going till you get some advice which makes sense to you. I certainly don't have all the answers and I don't believe that anyone does. If I've got to figure out something, I'll often take a step back and start thinking about ways to proceed. I've had to do that more than once with Ozzie. Take some time, think about it and come back later. There is no time limit.

During one lesson, I watched as a rider who was getting up on the horse, slipped off and stumbled back unbalanced to the ground as the stirrup leather dismantled itself. She started to get a little upset. I felt for her. No one wants to half fall off their horse at a lesson with their instructor watching and ten spectators in chairs outside the arena also watching on keenly. What was quite cool to watch though was while the lady was a little upset, due to the work she had been doing over the previous few days with the horse at this event, the horse was so chilled and grounded he just stood there with his head low and didn't bat an eye lid. He didn't even move one foot. He just stood there and looked at the human as if to say 'What on God's name are you doing now?'

Sometimes you've got to just say 'Crikey!!' and smile I reckon. I jumped on a big horse bareback out in Australia and then fell off about three seconds later. After a quick 'are you alright' all I got were jokes about the crack in my arse... sure what could I do but see the funny side!?

****

From talking to horse people, it's pretty common to feel pressure from other people watching what you are doing, from things you read in magazines, from what you hear other people saying, from what you watch other people doing with their horses.

You can think you're not jumping high enough, spending enough time, progressing fast enough or whatever. You need to somehow make peace in your own head, and not allow yourself to feel pressure from others. It doesn't matter that others think of you. What matters is what you think of yourself.

It does lead on though to the power of a compliment. Watch someone else doing something with their horse. Find something you like and then go up and compliment them!

'You've really got some nice transitions happening there.'

'Your horse is a credit to you, he's got great manners.'

'You've got a natural way with your horse.'

When someone says something like that to you, it doesn't cost them much, but gosh does it mean a lot to you! And it also takes away some of the pressure I mentioned above. I used to be terrible at taking compliments... 'Your horse is going nicely there,' and I'd say;

'Lord, he's ok now but he's not the easiest you know!'

One day I got paid a compliment. I had replied negatively putting myself down like the example above. The person who gave me the compliment looked at me crossly and said:

'Just shut up and take the compliment whether you think you deserve it or not. Just say thanks!'

He had a point. I went red and mumbled 'thank you'.

It was Friday night and I had an early flight from Dublin booked over to Gatwick airport the next morning. I had heard very good things about the trainer so I was looking forward to the weekend.

The plan for Friday evening was to go home, pack my stuff and sort out everything I needed to bring over, from a heavy coat to flip-flops, as you never knew what the weather would be like. So I duly went home, had tea and watched Coronation Street. At 9pm the whole house decided it was time to go out for a quiet drink.

The pub was about a half mile up the road and was known for its cocktails and comfy armchairs. That evening there was a country singer giving it socks up at the top of the room. He really looked like a cross between Hugh Grant and Jeremy Clarkson. To cut a long story short, roughly six hours later at about 3am on Saturday morning I arrived home after throwing some highly impressive moves on the dance floor, just in time for two hours sleep before the taxi for the airport was due at 5.30am. At 6am I was sitting in the airport looking fairly rough. At 7.50am I was pelting down the runway on a Ryanair Boeing 737-800 and at ten o'clock, fresh as a proverbial daisy, I hopped out of Gatwick airport, picked up the car and headed off to a beautiful farm in Sussex, arriving just in time for lunch.

My God the weather was beautiful! The place was perfect - lovely big arena, all of us sitting outside it in deckchairs under gazebo type structures, beautiful food and great company. All that was left was to settle in and watch how each horse and rider were progressing in the arena.

****

Working on longlines was a beautiful Friesian four year old which had previously been taught to over bend his head completely so his chin was tucked into his chest whenever he moved. He couldn't

134

move properly and his front end was all jammed up. The plan was to try and work on that, soften the horse up and get his chin unstuck from his chest. The plan was when the horse tucked his head in, the handler immediately put more pressure on the long lines. When the horse relaxed his head and didn't tuck it in, the handler just kept a light contact on the long lines. They walked around the arena repeating this.

Every time the horse tucked his head in - and then got more pressure on the reins as a result - you could nearly see him thinking 'Huh?? This isn't normal! What's going on?!'

He had two lessons a day. The first day I saw him he was extremely overbent roughly about 80% of the time. By the end of the second day, I'd say it was down to about 30%. I'd say in another few days of this work it would be nearly all but gone. This kind of work shows you that if you take a bit of time before you grab your horse from the field, figure out what your goal is and how you can explain things simply and consistently to your horse, how quickly they can learn new things. I guess I love the easy logic of it... we didn't want the over-bending so we communicated to the horse nicely that we didn't like it. We did like the normal relaxed head position so we communicated to him that this was right when he did it. Then we repeated this and watched as he figured it out and got better. It can be easy not to have a plan when you take your horse out, but if your goal every time you ride your horse is to get one little thing a bit better, imagine how cool your horse will be after 100, 1,000 or even 10,000 rides.

****

Next up in the arena was a little black horse. I hadn't seen the first two days, but there had been a bit of work done again on training this horse to respect the handler's personal space and on tidying up the groundwork manners. The initial work on Sunday was to get the horse listening to the handler. She tended to zone out and just wander around paying about 20% of her attention to the person.

135

When your horse isn't mentally with you and listening to you properly, neither of you are really that safe.

So the horse was asked to do a few circles at walk on a loose rope, the aim being to get her focused on the handler. When the horse focused, the handler relaxed and did nothing. When she started looking outside the arena and thinking that what was out there was more important than her handler, the handler started to make her move more, and created energy and attention to bring the horses attention back to her. Soon a switched off horse staring outside the arena had changed into a responsive interested horse who was following her handler around automatically with no lead rope pressure. Wherever the handler went the horse's head followed in the same direction.

There is something to be said for making sure your horse is 100% with you before to do some proper schooling! A good exercise is to ensure that when you are on the ground with your horse, you can keep your horse's attention on you for thirty seconds.

Next up was riding and creating softness. The rider was asked to start with a soft halt. The idea is that you pick up a light contact and just hold it. Wait. Your horse might do nothing, might pull against you, or might raise up their head to get out of it. Don't increase the contact, don't move your hands, just hold it and wait for softness.

When your horse gives his head a little and you feel the strain gone from the reins, immediately loosen them a little as a reward, or you can just hold them steady as your horse will give himself a reward, whichever option works better for you. Do this often enough and when you hop on and pick up the reins, your horse will automatically soften his mouth.

The idea is that now your horse is balanced – he could just as easily take a step forwards or take a step backwards, whatever you choose to do. With a lot of horses, when you sit up and take a light contact they immediately push their weight forward. Then you are not at the 50/50 forwards - backwards balance, you are about 80% forwards, 20% backwards, and so are off balance and not really ready for all manovres.

Once the soft halt was established, this was repeated from halt to backup. Once this was established, then it was time to start doing it in a walk starting with one step of softness. On Saturday this little horse was up to doing this for three steps in a row, and on Sunday it had built up to five or more steps of softness together in walk. Horses pick things up so quickly!

Their homework was to continue this at home in walk, slowly increasing the steps required with softness. There was a good rider onboard, as the rider must really concentrate on the horse to get those split second releases timed exactly right. It's quite easy. You just have to be to awake and thinking when you sit in the saddle.

****

I was down in Waterford a while back. We were doing some circling work with a horse. It's kind of different to normal lunging. The problem was that the whole time the horse was looking to the outside and while he was physically moving around that circle, he was paying very little attention mentally to his owner.

'How do you think this horse is going?' I asked his owner as the horse trotted around, stiff as a plank and head to the outside.

'Yep, he's going grand I think', she replied.

I nodded my head and thought about it.

'Would you mind if I took over for a minute?' I asked politely.

'Sure', she replied. I stepped into the circle and took over the long rope which was attached to the halter on the horse.

'OK, while your horse is physically doing what you ask, I don't think his heart is really in it and he's not really listening to you. I'm just going to see if I can change things a little...'

If you don't know something is possible then it is next to impossible to try to achieve it. I took over the twelve foot rope, and started to get the horse doing a bit more. Every time he'd zone out mentally and look out the window, straight away I was in there making noise and creating energy to get him to think 'gosh, what on earth is that girl doing in the middle of the circle, I'd better take a look'. Every time he would listen properly and relax and soften, then I would relax too and let him think about it. A second later when he went back to looking outside again and straightened his body, it was time for me to get his attention back again.

About four minutes later, we had gone from having a half asleep trot, with a horse who ignored me and stared out to the horizon, with a straight body and a tight lead rope, little bend in his body, to a much softer horse, with bend in his body, listening to me and able to react quicker when asked for different things. The lead rope was loose as his head was now looking in a little to me due to the softness and bend through his body, and he had started paying attention to what I was doing. Physically he looked like a different horse. He looked like an athlete ready for the next competition, not like a half ton animal who would rather be somewhere else. I handed him back to his owner.

'When he was walking and trotting around you he was only going through the motions... so you got the straight unbalanced body. His attention was on what was going on outside, the lead rope was tight, and he wasn't paying much attention to you. Can you see the difference in him now?'

The horse looked at me with big brown eyes so I gave him a rub. He was a cool horse.

138

'Yeah I do,' she replied. 'I never even knew you could do that. Wow. That was quite cool. I see how he was zoned out before.'

She took the rope and tried it then herself, and so I left her with some homework, this being one of the things to work on.

There may be a whole new world out there waiting for you to discover, but if you don't see a glimpse of it through an open door you might never know it is there. It's just another reason to keep learning and sharing information with others. You never know where you will end up.

23. The horsebox

When I bought Ozzie I didn't really know anything about him. I hadn't a clue if he was slow or fast on his feet, how clever he was or what bad habits he'd already picked up.

From the work I'd done so far I'd figured out that he was very touch sensitive. If you weren't sensitive in return at the beginning this would raise his emotions and he'd get scared quite quickly.

If you went striding up in a determined walk to pat him or pick up his foot, he'd get immediately worried and back away. He'd gotten used to Dad and me now, so what he needed was to get used to other people handling him. This would hopefully increase his emotional tolerance.

Ozzie was turning out to be a very smart horse. Once you gave him a bit of time and space to figure things out for himself, he was a hard worker, enjoyed getting things right, was really curious and loved learning new things.

When training a young horse curiosity is worth its weight in gold. I started to load Ozzie into the horsebox and to tell you the truth he did most of the work himself. This curiosity you want to maintain, and increase. The more curious a horse is, the less scared he will be. So when you meet something strange out riding, you will have a confident partner.

That day I was going to show Ozzie the horsebox. The plan wasn't to get him in it, but just to get him a little more comfortable and inquisitive with it. I drove the double box and jeep out to the centre of the paddock, and left it there, with the back ramp open. I went up and caught Ozzie, and as I brought him down to the round pen, he was already looking towards the horsebox with interest.

I walked him towards the box, past the box, and then away from the box. So while he was in the round pen, and I was doing his daily feet picking up, Ozzie was thinking 'what's in that box?' I had a curious horse on my hands.

What I wanted Ozzie to eventually do was to walk straight into the horse box on his own, while I stood outside the ramp area. Teaching this doesn't involve any sticks, ropes, panels, pushing or stress. What it does involve is a little patience and horse psychology. Because Ozzie hadn't previously been scared of the horsebox, I wanted to let him, being a curious horse, figure it out by himself.

****

I led Ozzie over near the horsebox and as expected, he stopped about four or five steps away from it, head up, ears pricked, looking towards it.

'What in God's name is that, Elaine?' Ozzie thought, and stared at the box for a short while.

'Just somewhere new, it's actually quite fun,' I replied, asking him to turn and walk in the opposite direction, still keeping that same 'safety' distance from the box. Ozzie was going to be the one who decided when he wanted to move closer, not me. Ozzie stood still, regarding it on a loose rope.

'It does seem kind of interesting alright. What's that yellow stuff that's in it?' he asked, taking a step closer by himself.

'That's straw', I replied confidently.

'Like that stuff in the stable?' he said. He thought about it for a minute. 'Seems alright. Maybe I should just have a look at it for you, check it's alright.'

141

As I stood still, Ozzie began a slow walk over towards the base of the horse box ramp. Gingerly, he reached out, arching his neck and sniffed the ramp, and then took his head away from it again.

'Good Ozzie, that was really brave of you. Because you were so good, we're going to have a rest.' I turned him away from the horsebox, and we walked back near the round pen. He stood quietly there as I gave him a rub. Every so often he'd look back towards the box.

'Elaine, I appreciate the rest but I wasn't finished yet with that box. There's more stuff to explore in it and I never got to check out all that straw for you, just the stuff at the bottom of the ramp. Can we go back over?' Ozzie looked back over towards the box again.

Never one to disappoint my horse, we headed back and this time, he walked quietly, on a loose rope, right up to the start of the ramp.

'Hey Elaine, look at these tail lights, those reflectors are cool!'

Ozzie had found the reflectors and lights on the right side of the box beside the ramp and was busy investigating.

'OK, hang on Elaine, there's more stuff here too. I'll just check it out for you,' Ozzie thought studiously. He switched his attention back to the ramp, and was soon nibbling and trying to bite the horizontal raised wooden bars on the ramp.

'This is cool!! I love eating stuff'. I left him to it for another minute, and then as a reward for being curious, I took him away back to the round pen for a rest.

'Hey, where are we going? I was just starting to have fun over there!' Ozzie, looking wistfully towards the horsebox, 'Can we go back over?'

After a minute or two, we headed back, and this time the back lights on the other side of the horsebox caught his eye, and he went over to sniff and investigate them.

Now I had a horse that was happy and relaxed at the foot of the ramp. The next step was to get his front feet on the ramp.

'Ozzie, if you eat those lights you're going to have to buy new ones and I don't think you can afford them,' I said. 'Come back over here and tell me what you think of this ramp.' I gently pulled on the rope and he wandered back over to me.

'This ramp?' he said. 'Well it's alright I guess' Oz replied. 'Let me just have another look.'

He started sniffing the start of the ramp, and after about two minutes of investigating, he was leaning over the ramp, neck long and arched, feet balancing together at the foot of the ramp, he started to sniff at the point where the ramp met the horsebox floor.

'Hey Elaine, I've found all this straw stuff again. I ate a bit of it, but it was a bit weird so I spat it out again. It's interesting though.' He had turned into Christopher Columbus.

'Well done, good work. Let's go back to the round pen and have another rest as a reward.' I took him back for his rest and rub, and while he enjoyed it, he was still looking back with interest towards the box.

'We're not finished for the day yet are we? I still want to check out that partition thing in the box. I can definitely smell that some other horses have been in there already. Can I go back *please* and see who it was? Please, pretty please?'

The plan was working quite well.

143

We went back over and I positioned Ozzie at the foot of the box. About two minutes later, one great horse hoof took a big step and landed nearly at the top of the ramp. Ozzie looked at me in surprise.

'Gosh, that was an odd noise,' he said, lifting his foot back off the ramp, and onto the grass again.

'It was a bit strange alright', I agreed. 'But you were very brave to try it, so let's have another rest.'

'OK' he replied, 'but only a short one. I'm in the middle of some exciting exploring work you know.'

I smiled to myself. 'OK Ozzie, that's a deal.'

A minute later we were back over, and soon (by himself) he put his two front feet on the ramp, and was busy investigating inside the box. After one of two more 'rests' away from the box, Ozzie had his two front feet at the top of the ramp, and his two hind feet just at the edge of the grass. He was standing there still, while I was rubbing his back and rump. A horse that goes into a box and comes back out like a bullet is no good. Standing still and relaxed with four feet on the ramp, is much better than having all four feet temporarily in the horsebox and bolting backwards.

We had made a lot of progress with Ozzie, and so I decided it was a good time to stop, give him a rub and bring him back out to the field. As I was walking him away, we headed on out past the jeep and horsebox, and the monkey was turning his head around back towards the box, as if to say, ' Aww we're not finished are we? I was just starting to have fun!'

If you can train your horse to 'want' to go into a horsebox, you'll always have a very easy horse to load. Like most things, if you've set their mind up properly, their body will follow.

As we were heading back out to the field, Ozzie caught sight of the bucket I had left by the gate. I'd had it out earlier in the field, and to my amusement, after an initial wariness, Ozzie had begun playing with it himself pushing and knocking it about like a toy.

He'd spotted it again now and pulled lightly on the lead rope as if to suggest we'd go over to it. We went over and Ozzie was delighted. Another toy to play with!! He smelt it over, nibbled at it, and then gently picked it up by the handle. He raised his head up in the air to normal level, and just stood there, with the bucket handle between his teeth looking pleased with himself.

Then he lowered his head and put the bucket down. After a few more nibbles, he then took hold of the rim, and again lifted the whole bucket into the air, the correct way up as if he was carrying something in it.

He stood still for maybe ten seconds, and then spotted something moving in the distance. Up came both his head and the bucket even further. What could I do but laugh.

Then to make matters worse, Dad, who was cutting the grass next door in the garden, did something to catch Ozzie's attention, and Ozzie swung his head around (with bucket still intact) and stared over at him, literally like a dog with a bowl in his mouth. I had bought a comedian! In the end I took hold of the rim of the bucket as well, and after a small tug of war, Ozzie let go and I was now the proud possessor of the bucket. When I left him back out to the paddock, I gave him a rub and took off his halter. As I was walking away, he turned around, looking at me, the horsebox and the bucket as if to say 'hey, come back soon alright?'

I tell you, horses can make you laugh but this guy was in a league of his own.

24. In the gym and on the bit.

'Oh my God I'm getting so lazy it's bloody ridiculous,' I muttered to myself while slumped in front of the television.

Up until the previous November I worked fulltime as a software manager in Sligo. Working all day in an office, I found that I got a bit lazy when it was dark by 5pm and my good intentions to stay fit were rapidly evaporating.

Every few years in my life I tend to do something unexpected. I had been in work for the last three years and I was getting itchy feet again. The prospect of going back out to Australia and New Zealand for a second time had become very appealing.

The friends and fellow travelers I had met out there the last time were the kind of people you'd be proud to say you knew. Australia had outback tequila snorting, daredevil action and some kind of pub game which involved pint glasses on your elbows while you crawled on all fours against your competitors. New Zealand hit back with homemade bazooka competitions, wild pig hunting and the secret art of 4x4 driving with only two wheels in contact at any time with the mountain you were driving over. And I haven't even mentioned jumping off anything attached to an elastic rope or parachute just for the hell of it. 'Up a mountain and down a beer' as I saw on one t-shirt.

When I arrived over in New Zealand in December I was working in the natural horsemanship yard with Cathy, teaching horsemanship and bringing locals and tourists on treks through the South Alps. The ten or so horses they owned lived in a lush green valley between two hills in this Lord of the Rings style country.

The upside was it was beautiful and only rained every second day. The downside was that it meant a good hill walk every morning and evening to bring the horses up and down. I started to get quite fit. A month later I headed on to north Brisbane in Australia for more daily riding and training. Six weeks after that and I hopped off the huge airbus plane which had brought me back from Brisbane, through Singapore airport, London Heathrow, and then Shannon. I was as fit as a fiddle.

I had been back in Tipperary a few weeks at this stage, and with the rotten weather and Ozzie at the early stages of groundwork, I started to lose fitness. So I decided to take the bull by the horns, and booked myself into a gym.

I hate gyms.

The last gym I joined in Dublin city centre, it depressed me so much I quit after four weeks. I'd found a small local place where the idea was that you did half an hour's work, about three days a week. I can't explain it, but I actually found myself enjoying it. The music helped a lot I think. You can't go too far wrong when you're dancing.

While my body was working my head would often start thinking about things by itself. I'd often find myself putting some logic around things that had happened.

That day I started to think about a conversation I had about what people do to get their horses 'on the bit'. The lady I talked to mentioned in passing that she had seen horses out loose in a paddock with side reins on. To me this is abuse, not to mention a dangerous accident waiting to happen. Going on the bit was a challenge for me when I was younger. When I was growing up, I went through three ponies of various sizes.

Breezly was tiny, loved eating and didn't like moving. His favourite position was lying down asleep in the sunshine. I don't think I ever got him to trot! He was the original energy conservator.

When I actually did want to trot, we got Thady. He was a little bigger and disliked whips but was a great showjumper and hunter, and I loved him to bits. I never rode with a whip.

When I was twelve it was time to look for a pony with longer legs than I had. Pepsi appeared, an experienced showjumper and with the exception of a few bolting issues at the beginning, he was routinely used as the demo horse in pony club. Anyone who had a tricky pony used to borrow him to do their road test on. He was a much loved institution.

Once I was fourteen or fifteen years old I moved onto Mum's horse, Cinderella. She was gorgeous, with a white nose, loved her jumping and never knocked a pole. In the exam system which I had been progressing through, we were arriving at the stage where dressage and going 'on the bit' was becoming more important. Cinderella bless her, while great at jumping and hunting, and a lovely all rounder, had never really done much dressage or lateral work or any of this 'on the bit' business. She couldn't see the point of working in circles for an hour or two. Now I'd probably agree with her.

Initially to get her 'on the bit', I was advised to work on circles, creating impulsion with the hind-end, and then pulling a fair bit on the reins to 'hold in' the impulsion, and also to force her head down and in. I remember one day saying to my instructor after about an hour that I needed to stop as the palms of my hands were bleeding and raw from pulling. I don't want to think about what Cinderalla's mouth was like.

After that, it was decided that a double bridle might help, and so for the sake of the exams I wanted to do, I rode my horse - with her soft mouth - in a double bridle and did my utmost to achieve that 'on the bit' look.

The good news was that we passed the exam. The bad news was that it was worth nothing to me.

148

I felt really guilty about what I'd done to Cinders, swore I'd never do it again and threw away the double bridle. If this pain, force and pressure was what it took to get a horse 'on the bit', then I wanted no part in it. It was only a few years later in a dusty round pen in Caboolture, that I learned how easy 'on the bit' can be.

To prepare an athlete you first need to make sure their whole body is soft, supple and flexible, and ready for your chosen equestrian discipline, whether it's western, hunting, jumping, dressage or polocrosse. Imagine your horse is a gymnast. Before every performance, a gymnast needs to warm up their muscles and make sure every part of their body is flexible. It's the same for horses.

'On the bit' isn't just one thing. It's actually lots of small things. When you put them all together, then you get the rounded back, the engaged hindquarters, the vertical head flexion, the softness and suppleness and ease of movement that all come together under the 'on the bit' banner. The thing about training a horse is that it's not rocket science. It's actually pretty logical.

First up, supple up your horse's body. Move the back legs sideways to free up the hind end. Move the front legs sideways to loosen up the shoulders. Backup your horse to make sure his front legs aren't planted into the ground and get the weight off the front end. Do some sidepassing to teach your horse that when one leg goes on you want bend and softness through his body, not just speed. Bend his neck while his feet stand still to loosen up his front end. You can do this all on the ground, and they are all pretty easy. You just need to practice them a little. If you've got all these things done separately, you should then be able to put them together. You're now riding a horse who can balance on a bend or circle with his body in the same arc as the circle. His feet are under his body and he's not going around like a motorbike which is about to fall over sideways.

Next up you want to relax his jaw. You can do this in halt to start off. Pick up a light contact. Hold it and wait. Your horse will probably reposition his head, either up or down slightly or he might pull against your rein. Sit there, wait and keep your hands completely still like a wooden post. When he relaxes his jaw, loosen that inside rein completely. It's really easy to see this on the ground, so if you've a helper nearby that's cool.

In the end your horse's shoulders are free, so his back is able to round and you have lovely athletic long strides, rather than pony type steps. Working on the circle, his body is arced around your inside leg, and his head and neck are turned slightly inwards.

Your horse has started to figure out that if he relaxes his jaw that you will release all pressure on the reins. Now he is inclined to do this by himself, rounding his back, and his hindquarters start coming in under him a lot more than before.

From your perspective, light pressure with your inside leg automatically results in an arced horse. When your horse comes down 'on the bit', you've actually got no weight at all in your hands. Your horse is soft, supple, balanced, engaged, rounded, flexible, free moving and 'on the bit'. While I say 'on the bit' you can do all of this bitless.

With Ozzie, we'd some of this done already. On the ground we'd already done hindquarter yield, forequarter yield, sidepass, and lateral flexion. The next step for him was to do a good 'normal' walk, trot and canter. After that, it wouldn't be too difficult to encourage 'on the bit' as most of the preparation we'd done already.

25. Sometimes you have to teach things twice.

It was time to get Ozzie's feet done and so our farrier was expected out to our house on Friday morning. I would have liked to have been there but I'd got a new I.T. job in Dublin so I was busy house hunting up there. House hunting in Dublin was a nightmare. I was looking for somewhere in Ringsend, the city centre or Clontarf and I was routinely one of twenty or more people, boomeranging in and out of small grimy rooms offered at over €650 a month, surrounded by the oddest house mates imaginable in decidedly rough sections of Dublin. The over-inflated house prices had meant the country had gone mad.

I rang home at lunch time on Friday to hear what happened. Ozzie had been a star. He had been a bit tricky to catch as all of my halters were in my car, so Dad had to use a bulky one we had which Ozzie hadn't seen before so he was a bit suspicious.

After that he stood like a rock as if he had been doing it all his life. Dad told Joseph that we suspected that Ozzie had been sedated before his feet were done the last time and Joseph agreed saying it was a common enough procedure. When we were talking to Ozzie's previous owner at the sales, he had said that Ozzie 'just needed a bit of handling'. That had turned out to be true enough.

I was delighted though – the first time with our farrier and Ozzie had behaved perfectly. It was a small step in the bigger scheme of things, but a huge achievement for Ozzie, compared to what he had been like and how much time we had to put into him to get him to this stage.

****

When I was growing up we always had three or four horses or ponies on our farm. Most of these were signed up to stay with us for life and so we got very familiar with their individual likes,

151

dislikes and quirks. Chester our first big hunter, had a great ability to blow his nose. I remember meeting him for the first time, when he was in a field which we had driven down to, and as a seven year old looking up into the eyes of this huge beast, I was mesmerized. Then he blew his nose and a huge amount of snot flew out all over me. It was a bit disgusting but I didn't mind at all. I was enthralled by this big horse.

Cinderella used to always rush out of horseboxes when loading. It was what you'd describe as a 'quirk' but as it didn't really cause any problems (we'd just stand back and give her a loose rope) we didn't bother to do anything about it.

Thady's 'quirk' was that he was terrified of whips and anyone waving a stick. But it wasn't an issue for us. He didn't like them so we never used them.

I bet that if you look closely, all horses have their quirks – maybe being difficult to catch, awkward to load, hard to lead, rushing over fences, scared of plastic bags or whatever. Some of these things, you can probably manage and live with as we did with our horses. But why live with a problem? Maybe you could look on it as an opportunity to work on a training skill.

****

Over the past four or five days, I'd noticed that Ozzie was starting to develop a little quirk. He was becoming a little more awkward to catch. He was not bad to catch but I could see him getting fractionally more evasive each day, and in about a week or two I could see myself having to do laps of the field which I don't fancy as I really am quite lazy.

When we did our initial training, Ozzie would stand still facing me as I approached and I had no issues putting on the headcollar.

Recently when I approached him he stood for a minute and then moved off at a walk away from me. I'd slap my jeans to get him to turn around and face me (which he would) but if I tried to put the halter on him he would walk away again. I could still catch him easily by looping the lead rope first over his neck, but this was something which I wanted to fix before it got more awkward. Horses do learn what you teach them, but sometimes they can be inclined to forget bits of it as well. It was time for some retraining.

When I had taught Ozzie to be caught the first time, I hadn't asked him to turn his head to me before I put the halter on. This was where we had started to come unstuck now.

So I broke this catching task down into a few parts:

First Ozzie had to stand still beside me. Then I wanted to be able to put my hand on his nose and turn his head around to me. Then while still holding Ozzie's nose around, I put on the halter.

As Ozzie was haltered and standing beside me already I was going to start with the lateral flexion, so that if he moved away I could ask him to come back with the lead rope.

I put my hand over his nose and the split second he stopped pulling against me I let go and gave him a rub. After about ten minutes, he had improved on both sides. Next up was to take off the halter.

At the beginning, Ozzie would walk away from me around the pen, and then to show him this wasn't what I wanted, I'd 'whoosh' him away. Any time he'd look towards me or walk towards me, I showed him that this was what I wanted, by looking down, becoming quiet and still. He'd done this before so he knew the drill.

To get me to stop bugging him, all he had to do was walk up to me for a rub and a rest. To begin with he wasn't too bad, but as he was standing beside me, any effort to rub past his shoulder – towards his head – resulted in him turning away from me and walking away. So it was back to the beginning again as I whooshed him around the pen, waiting again for him to look or move towards me.

After a while Ozzie came back into me and stood quietly. As he stood still and I stood on his near side (which he's more comfortable with) I put my hand on his nose three times and got him to get his head around to me, without him moving any feet at all. We were getting better!

Another thing I did notice about Ozzie as he walked around me was that he was now 'tracking up'. This means the hind foot lands roughly in the place the forefoot had just been.

When judging a horse's conformation and movement, I would place a lot of emphasis on correct conformation and ease of movement. Ozzie had very good conformation which was partly the reason why we bought him in the first place, and also when he walked and trotted, it looked effortless, like the trot of a much larger horse. Nice and easy.

Sean our neighbour had mentioned that while Ozzie was indeed nicely put together, and trotted up well, he didn't 'track up'. He said that this was a pity, as it was something a lot of buyers would potentially look for in a dressage or event horse. When he had been looking at Ozzie a few weeks previously, Ozzie had been a bit spooky and uptight so his head was held quite high. I mentioned at the time that this might have an impact on his gait, but it didn't really hold much water with our friend.

What was really interesting when watching Ozzie circle around me, was that he was tracking up beautifully in a slow walk and trot as his hind feet regularly landed where the forefoot had been.

What had changed? Ozzie was relaxed so his head was down. His back had started to round and his hindquarters had started to come in underneath him, meaning he would stretch his hind feet further forward now. In doing all of this he was now tracking up beautifully. Bio-engineering is a great thing. I guess I was now training a dressage prospect.

In the end I did catch him and turned his head around to me ten times in a row – five on each side. So far so good.

****

After lunch I headed out again, and Ozzie was ready and waiting. I entered the round pen and walked a few steps away from him, and soon I had a grey head resting on my shoulder. This time I also had my halter and lead rope hanging over my arm. For about ten minutes, on the near side, I worked on Ozzie standing quietly beside me, lateral flexion, and then putting on the halter while still holding his nose towards me. He was great. So much so that I put the halter on him six times in between him following me loose around the pen in a circle and a figure of eight. We were definitely getting better. I left him back out in the paddock.

That evening, the weather having reverted to its normal unpredictable self was threatening rain and the wind was picking up. Ozzie spotted me as I wandered down checking the other horses, and he started walking up towards me.

He stood quietly as I entered the paddock and remained stationary as I walked towards him. Then he turned and walked away (he obviously hadn't read that part of the plan yet) and so I slapped my hand against my jeans, and he turned around and looked at me.

Then I walked up to him as he stood still, rubbed his face and his nose, turned his nose towards me and put on the halter. Even though he had walked away from me, I was quite happy that once I was beside him, he had no problem with me bringing his neck around to me. This was something I wouldn't have been able to do two days previously.

155

After a rub, I took the halter off, and asked him to follow me in a half circle, while loose. When I stopped this time, he stopped with me and the halter went back on and off another two times without incident. We were improving. Another rub for Ozzie and I took the halter off again.

As Ozzie stood there, suddenly a bicycle appeared in front of the house and simultaneously a herd of cattle started to gallop down from the pond towards where the other horses were standing. Ozzie pricked up his ears and followed both events with curiosity. Would he stand now for the halter, with all the distractions??

He did. Perfectly.

The halter went on and off twice again. So while he had tried to walk away from me twice, which we had addressed, once he was actually standing beside me, by using lateral flexion it had been easy to put on the halter. No more wandering off once the halter started to approach his face. It was a good morning's work. My little horse was coming on nicely.

26. Eight weeks and time to update our goals.

Ozzie had been out in the big field for two days with his bovine friends and seemed quite content. The downside was that his carpet had disappeared so he couldn't amuse himself by dragging it about. On a positive note there were a lot of great watery brown cow-dungs around the field which he had become quite proficient in lying on and rolling around in. It is awful stuff to get off a horse and it really sticks into their mane and tail hair, making a right mess. On inspection that day, Ozzie had one clean grey side, and one beautifully smelly cowdung brown side. And of course the obligatory brown eye area and a blob of poo in his forelock.

'You're not quite Ireland's Next Top Model are you Ozzie?' I asked him.

He looked back at me blankly. Surely I knew all horses were gorgeous no matter how much muck they were covered in?

One thing which I had been wondering about was trying to figure out if Ozzie was clever or if he wasn't. Eight weeks was a long time to get to where we were and I had wondered maybe if it was because I had taken things so slowly, or was it because he took a while to pick things up? I was chatting to a friend of mine and she remarked that what I did in eight weeks, had taken her eight months to do with her horse, who had been really badly handled before she got her. It made me realise that you can only start where your horse is. If you've got a horse who doesn't have many foundations in place, well then it is just going to take time to put them in. There is no use comparing your horse to another horse who has had a few years of brilliant handling already under his belt.

But back to Ozzie and his learning ability. From the start he had always been mentally with me and really interested in what's going on everywhere. He didn't tend to drift off into his own world very much which made my life easier as he was alert and awake when we did stuff together.

One day I had been playing with my long stick which had a piece of string attached to the end of it. I was rubbing it up his neck, and around his face. At one point I rested it between his ears so the string draped down the side of his face. He shook his head and the stick slid off away from his face. I didn't think too much of it and just put the end of the stick back between his ears. Again, he shook it off. The next time I moved the stick near his ears, he started to move away. 'Bugger' I thought. I just realised that in fifteen seconds I had started to teach my horse to be headshy. But how could Ozzie learn how to be headshy in fifteen seconds, yet take more than four weeks to learn how to let me pick his feet up? Something didn't add up here. I figured it out eventually though.

You can get either a response or a reaction from your horse. A response is thoughtful and measured and involves your horse figuring out what's going on calmly in an environment without fear, worry or panic. Responses take time and repetition to become normal behaviour.

A reaction is what happens when someone taps the front of your knee and it pings up by itself. There is no measured thought behind it. There is no calmness and it's more likely to occur when the horse is stressed, panicked or nervous. Reactions become normal behaviour very quickly. Because there's no measured thought behind them, they usually include the horse doing stuff we don't want.

After all my thought I figured I had a horse who needed extra time to put in the foundations, that we were doing well on responses and trying to avoid too many reactions, and that Ozzie still probably learned stuff faster than I did.

Frank and Deirdre were both coming over for lunch that day and were eager to see what I'd done with Ozzie since the last time they

158

had seen him. After lunch, I decided that I'd combine a mini-demo with our fourth time in the saddle. So with my halter under my arm I set off to catch Ozzie in the field. I walked up to him, rubbed his shoulder, rubbed his face, turned his head around to me, and put on the halter. He stood as if he had been doing it all his life. The catching 'retraining' we had done had paid off.

Ozzie was put into the round pen which was still looking like a high class golf course thanks to Dad's lawn-mowering and I went back up to the house to get my saddle, hat and plastic bag on a stick, and to let everyone know that the demo was about to start.

'How's he going Elaine?' Frank enquired as we walked outside.

'Not too bad thanks Frank. I've been up in Dublin for a bit so we haven't done a lot recently, but he's not too bad.'

The last time I had been in the saddle was probably near enough to two weeks ago, so my demo consisted of asking Ozzie to follow me around while loose in the round pen, doing big circles and changes of direction, a bit of rope twirling and plastic bag waving, feet picking up, saddling up, mounting, backup lightly, lateral flexion, hindquarter yields and then walking around with a few rein changes. Ozzie was a star. I thought he'd be a bit anxious or nervous as Frank and Deirdre were standing right outside the round pen but Ozzie wasn't bothered in the least.

'I was watching that horse channel on the television. Have you seen it?' Frank enquired.

I shook my head. 'Nope, not yet.'

'They do some amazing things on it. I wouldn't have believed it was possible only that I saw the stuff you'd done with Ozzie early on.'

'He's a lovely horse Elaine,' Deirdre added. 'He's a real credit to you. Did it take long to get him like this?'

I smiled and nodded. 'It took a while alright, but it was good fun.'

When Ozzie was loose in the round pen he stuck to me like glue. Wherever I went, he went. Then he stood relaxed as we threw ropes and plastic bags around, and all four feet were picked up without any resistance at all. Then on went the tack from the far side, a few circles in walk before the girth was fully tightened, and then after a few (planned) hops, I got on from the near side. He stood like a gentleman.

We did some more standing still, backup, a hindquarter yield on either side, a short walk in both directions around the pen, and then I dismounted on the far side. My riding goal for the day had been just to get back in the saddle and remind him what it was all about. He was very focused on me throughout, and behaved very well.

After I had dismounted Deirdre put her hand over the fence to offer Ozzie some freshly picked grass. The old Ozzie would have back-peddled away from her as far as he possibly could.

The new Ozzie sniffed Deirdre's hand and then ate some of the grass she was holding. Soon he was standing there looking quite pleased with himself as Deirdre rubbed his nose.

Where was the scared, anxious and untouchable horse that I had bought eight weeks ago? I now owned a different horse!

One thing that Deirdre commented on as we were talking about Ozzie later was that she was so impressed with the confidence that Ozzie had in me. It was true. Ozzie really had come out of himself a lot and was showing that he was a lot happier around people, and not just me, but around strangers too, who he had always been very wary of. My horse had indeed changed, a little on the outside thanks to the good grass and a lot on the inside.

This got me thinking that maybe I needed to change my training 'why's and 'how's' too. This had crossed my mind a few days earlier when I was making a short video of Ozzie to send out to Brad in Australia to show him how we were getting on.

I was looking forward to recording me picking up his feet. I was quite proud of how good he had got at it, particularly as he had initially been so bad at it. The little minx had other ideas though and what started out as a 'serious horse training' video ended up like something you'd see on 'Candid Camera' or 'You've Been Framed'.

Ozzie had been standing quietly on a loose rein. Standing beside him, I had rubbed his near shoulder, and then rubbed his near leg as far as his fetlock, without any complaint. I then asked Ozzie to pick up his near fore by increasing the pressure a little on his fetlock, and without any fuss, up came the foot. At this stage I could also feel Ozzie's nose which was now turned around towards me, smelling the end of my t-shirt.

If I'd been looking at him, I'd say I'd have seen a cheeky grin and a twinkle in his eye, and in the next second, I got a beautiful nip on my derriere! I wasn't going to put his foot down so I had to resort to an unladylike 'wiggle' of that area, to get him to move his head away, which he duly did. What a messer of a horse. And every moment of it caught on high definition video. While I probably haven't done it justice in my description, it's a true comic moment to watch. So much for the plan!

In my quest to turn an uncooperative anxious spooky horse into a confident, well balanced and relaxed horse, I had forgotten to stop teaching Ozzie once I had reached my goal.

Ozzie was completely correct in nipping me. I'm been so concerned initially with developing Ozzie's confidence and tolerance around people, that I hadn't noticed I had been so focused that I hadn't realised that Ozzie had learned what I wanted to teach him. As there's no point teaching a horse something he already knows (they get bored or you end up teaching them something else entirely as happened to me) it was time I updated my goals. I needed to re-examine my student's abilities and then draw up a plan of action for the next few weeks.

Number one on the list was no nudging or nibbling of any kind. That should soon get rid of the nips.

Number two on the list was to now treat Ozzie as a confident green horse, not as a scared blank slate.

Number three on the list was to take a well deserved break from the groundwork, which we had nearly finished anyway.

And number four on the list was to get back into the saddle after our little break and have some fun, as I had planned to do. I was looking forward to it already.

27. Dressage

I had heard on the grapevine there was going to be a very good dressage clinic happening over in England, so at the woeful hour of 4.40am on a dark Friday morning I dragged myself out of bed to catch the 6.30am flight over to Bristol. I did seem to be getting quite fond of Dublin airport. I arrived at the clinic at 9.30am to some surprisingly nice weather in Wiltshire. To ride in the clinic you had to be able to ride your horse without a bridle, halter or reins. From here everyone would be working on improving their dressage.

There was a nice mixture of horses from warmbloods to some coloureds (one gorgeous big coloured who floated across the ground, I wanted to bring home), a pony or two and some Irish hunter, TBs and Irish draft cross types.

When I arrived everyone was gathered in the barn and all the riders were talking about what they wanted to achieve from the clinic.

'I'd like to resolve some issues with contact. When I ride without the reins everything is perfect, then when I pick them up my problems start.'

The instructor nodded.

'Sure,' she smiled, 'we can do something there'.

The next person added in their aim.

'I'd like to help motivate my horse. At times he can he quite hard work to keep going.'

'OK, good,' the instructor replied.

Next was one of the two men who had been brave enough to come along.

'Well,' he said. 'My goal for this clinic is to be able to wear jodhpurs and compete!'

The whole room cracked up. The instructor threw her eyes up to heaven and grinned.

'We'll see what we can do!'

In total, most of the riders had similar goals. Working on riding with reins to the same standard they did their bridleless work was a common goal.

So what do the reins communicate? You don't need them to stop, turn or steer your horse, as all the riders present could do all of these without any reins. The instructor proposed that the reins are used as a circle of energy and feel. They are another point of communication and we can get information from them. One thing which they are really good for is to indicate subtle changes in head direction. The aim of dressage is to create healthy biomechanics. This rang a big bell with me as I don't like seeing horses pulled down within an inch of their lives to create an outline. I liked her style.

But where does all of this dressage business start??? That day the plan was to start with a 'let loose' posture. This is also a spinal stretch posture. So the horse's whole topline is stretched, arching like a rainbow from one end to the other.

Energy plus relaxation equals power.

So first up, you are looking for big, loose, free, confident horses. You will use a mixture of energy and relaxation (rests as rewards) to get it. The idea is you've a stretched horse and once you pick up the reins the horse can still feel like he can stretch and will stay big.

164

When you're working a horse you want to be able to turn every drop of energy into power.

If you have a horse which is a bit lazy, don't circle him in trot for ages as your horse might just think, 'ahh what's the point?, I'm bored and tired.' Only ask for short bits of good trot, and make things fun for all. Teach the horse that if he does offer a really nice energetic gait, he won't then always have to do it for ages and regret he offered it in the first place. Create a flow of energy, without any held tension. Horses need to know they can be powerful and go forward.

- You have to know what you want.
- You have to be able to analyse what you're getting
- Then you have to be able to compare the two.

The sun came out! If you can get your horse to completely relax, you'll find he will actually get much better at going then as well.

One thing to watch out for is after you do a movement, be aware that your horse doesn't finish up with a lot of weight on his inside foreleg which can happen.

That afternoon it was time to play with the gaits. All the horses were asked to try out walk and trot. Each was to do the slowest version they could do and then do the fastest version they could do. Then they were asked to find a version in between 'too fast' and 'too slow' that was just right. They did this with a demo horse, so after going very slow and then very fast, they figured out the trot they wanted from the horse was one shade faster than the trot the horse was currently offering. If you have a black and white, you can mix the two to get your perfect shade of grey. It did make sense.

She reckoned that you can train to grand prix bitless. When you use the bit, you are going inside the horse so it's a really subtle intimate communication.

165

It is very hard for humans to use their hands and arms and NOT tense up their body automatically and introduce pressure.

Think of it like dancing. Freestyle (with no bridle or reins) dancing is when you stand near someone, but you both dance on your own. It is fun, and it doesn't really matter if your partner can't dance. You can still boogie away to your heart's content.

When you ride with reins you have a closer contact with your partner. This is like ballroom dancing when you dance together with the girl having one hand on guys shoulder, and the other hand in his hand. More points of contact and more communication.

If your partner is good, this can be amazing and he can make you look REALLY good. If your partner is terrible, everything is just awful, even worse than if your partner was bad when dancing freestyle. Imagine the bit is actually just your two index fingers, one at each side of your horse's mouth.

In dressage the goal is a happy horse. But this isn't just a future goal - you should also start with a happy horse and rider.

When you pick up the reins and it all goes pear-shaped, fix things using your seat not your reins. Sometimes when you've got your reins in your hands you forget about the other cues you can also use. When you are riding, you want to feel your horse's hocks in your hands. Good cross training would be tai chi, salsa or ballroom dancing.

A while back the instructor was teaching a grand prix dressage rider in a New York clinic. The rider would not drop the reins. She wanted to work on softness, lightness and pirouettes. When she did drop the reins the horse wouldn't stand still, but would walk forward instead. This rider also had two big dogs. The instructor asked her how she trained her dogs to sit. She said she used a verbal cue and backed it up with a touch to get dog to sit, the moved away from the dog as he stayed sitting.

Instructor: 'Why'd you move away from the dog?'

Rider: 'Well I couldn't sit there holding him in one place all day! He had to learn how to do it by himself.'

Then the penny dropped that she might need to do the same with her horse as well.

I got chatting to the lady sitting on the horse shavings beside me.

'Isn't it odd how when you do one rein stuff on the ground it's so good, but when you use the one rein from the saddle it's not so good?'

She nodded her head in agreement.

'We were chatting about this last night actually,' she replied as some light rain started to fall.

'The difference is in the rider. You can be really confident on the ground when working a horse and it comes through your energy and body language, feel, timing, cues and so on. In the saddle maybe you're not that 100% confident person you were on the ground. So it doesn't work as well. I know someone who took her big warmblood to a different clinic. They did some really nice work in trot. The instructor that day said 'now that was a nice trot!' I was chatting to the rider later on and she felt like she was being run away with during that trot.'

'I see what you mean,' I replied. 'I think you could be right.'

They continued on and by day three everyone was doing some really nice extension exercises and lateral work, moving from walk into various manoeuvres and keeping a regular rhythm. For the movements where you really had to think about what you were doing, they started at walk then halted in the various positions. This was a really nice way to do it as you can take as much time as you need to get it right. They did some really nice walk pirouettes,

167

and you could see how you could progress on from there to some really nice work.

One other cool thing was working on having the horse in perfect balance, ready for anything. In another clinic earlier that summer, I'd seen horses work on being in balance in halt, so their body was equally ready to move either backwards or forwards.

What was really interesting today was that they were doing the same thing in this clinic, but in walk and trot as well. The idea is that when (for example) in walk, you have your horse in a state of readiness, to either halt or trot. If you think your horse will find it easier to move to trot rather than halt, then he is not really balanced yet. But if you think he will find it equally easy to either halt or trot, then you've got it. You can build this into things like moving from a walk to a backup without stopping at all and keeping the rhythm, or going forward - back - forward - back - forward as well.

You are looking for 'preparedness' like a tennis player in perfect athletic balance, in the middle of the tennis court waiting to see if the next ball will go to the right or to the left. The goal is that you want to know what it feels like to be prepared. So find the trot when your horse is ready to canter, and then backup.

A few years ago the instructor had a remedial dressage horse who used to rear a lot. Nine months later after a lot of retraining she was doing piaffe with the horse and decided to play around with this a little. She asked the horse to sit down on hocks and increase energy. The horse did as asked and reared straight up. Once she checked she was ok she had to think quickly about how she was going to react to this. When the horse came down, she rubbed the horse and told him that was the best rear ever! She had asked the horse for it so he was only doing as he was told to do. She knew she was going into the danger zone. After the rear, horse had expected bad things to happen to him. If they had, the vicious rearing cycle would probably have started again. Instead he got a rub. They continued the session and did some lovely piaffes and passages and then walked in home on a loose rein. That rub after the rear had been the right reaction.

I flew home that Monday evening. It had been a very enjoyable weekend.

28. Think for yourself. Day six in the saddle.

I was fairly busy with my job in Dublin sorting out crashed servers and meeting publishing deadlines, but every weekend I tried my best to make it down to see Ozzie. In Tipperary, the riding had been going pretty well. One of the small things which had started to worry me a bit though was when Ozzie decided he couldn't do as I asked for whatever reason (horse fly was about to land on him or whatever), he had started to refuse to do as asked. On the ground I could push him through it, but once or twice in the riding he'd done the same and started the odd small mini-rear which I rode him through or found a way around. It wasn't a big issue and I reckoned the more work we did, the more he'd realise there was no point arguing as he'd always end up doing as I asked anyway. I guess it was also easier to ignore the issue as I didn't really have a good plan formed, so as long as the issue didn't arise too often, I hoped it would sort itself out.

I'd been at a local horse breeding course over the past few weeks with some other local Tipperary horse breeders and farmers. It was a nice mix and the shared novelty of being students again had bonded us into a strong, funny and irreverent group. Between all of us combined, we held hundreds of years of horse experience and knowledge.

One morning, one of the participants was talking about a new horse he had. The horse was pretty unhandled and it was the first day he had got the headcollar off and then back onto the horse. He was so pleased about it. As he talked about this horse his face lit up and his eyes shone with pride in his horse's achievement. But it wasn't really the fact that he could now put a headcollar on his horse, it was all about the increased trust and confidence his actions over the previous weeks had created which had led to this situation. Putting on the halter was just a physical example of how much trust and understanding had been established between both

170

of them. Having someone like you and trust you can mean a lot to a person.

There's so much potential for success when bringing on horses and often it's the things most people with older made horses take for granted – like putting on a headcollar, picking up feet, a grey nose coming over tentatively to sniff your coat, catching your horse, or even just being able to sit in the saddle – that result in your proudest moments as a horse trainer. Doing stuff in your horse's time is so important.

****

By the end of the previous day's session Ozzie could walk a lap on both reins, but he was noticeably better on the left rein. It also seemed that Ozzie had been thinking things through as well as catching forty winks since I saw him the day before.

We picked up all four feet in the round pen as usual, put on the saddle, walked him around with a 'just tight enough' girth, then tightened the girth properly after the walk and I hopped on without any bother. Ozzie was very relaxed again with his ears forward and head low. We stood still for a few minutes at first just enjoying each other's company.

I asked Ozzie to turn his head around to me a little and then we set off on a small circle in that direction. He was much better than the previous day, with very few unauthorised stops and soon he was walking small figures of eight, changing the flexion every time we passed through the centre. I didn't just want Ozzie to be able to walk. I wanted him to be able to walk on a circle with bend, softness and suppleness, right from the very beginning. Start as I meant to continue. As we went around, he was great on both reins, unlike the day before when they had been more uneven.

The figures of eights involved circles in both directions and the bend in his body followed the arc of the circle he was on. Soon his

171

head started to lower as he relaxed, and his ribs softened. Even though it was only the first time he'd walked on nicely on both reins, we were also starting to get a nice outline, his feet were tracking up as his hind end was coming underneath him, and because his shoulders were free moving, his head was lowering and his back was starting to round a little.

Every so often I'd ask him to stop and backup, and then he'd get a rub and a rest. It was another unseasonably warm day, and there were lots of flies about. As we stood still having a rest, Ozzie would put his face right down, near the flies which were dancing a few inches above the carpet of grass he was standing on.

Standing there with a look of concentration on his face, pricked ears, an arched neck and glossy mane and tail, he could have been an Arabian without a doubt. What a character. Nothing, not even a fly, got past him. Ozzie was tuned into absolutely everything that was going on around him.

As he was being so good, I thought we'd try some sidepassing and some forequarter yields for the first time in the saddle from a halt. While we weren't perfect the first time, we got some lovely lateral moves for both and I really couldn't have asked for anything more. So we stopped and relaxed again, and this time Ozzie put his head right down low, and just stood there very relaxed on a loose rein, enjoying the sunshine. Honestly he was like a horse who had done all of this a thousand times before. He was very trusting, confident, proud of himself, I dare say, and completely comfortable with me in the saddle, Dad watching on, and the flies buzzing around.

I gave him a rub, dismounted and took off his tack. As we walked back out Ozzie made a beeline for a white upright and started to play with it. After that, I brought him over to the football, which he sniffed and nibbled and then I dribbled over towards the field as Ozzie followed me with interest. Boys do love their football. I left him out, and after contemplating a roll, he decided against it and stood beside the paddock, watching me walk back up towards the house. If you can turn your training into something fun and enjoyable, you might find that your horse enjoys it nearly as much as you do.

****

In the Sunday papers there is usually a section where they interview someone famous and ask them about their first memory, first words, first influence, first big break or the first album they bought. While some people confidently say that they can remember incidents when they were one or two years old, I reckon I must have a terrible memory! When I try to think backwards, my first memory seems to be when I was about six years old. I had just got my first pony, Breezely, and I used to go over to New Inn for riding lessons with my riding teacher, Mr. Dooley.

I used to love those lessons. Mr. Dooley had an enclosed oval paddock so it was there that I learned the basics of how to stay on a pony, to ride gently without pulling or kicking, and how to jump over small fences. The strange beautiful horses they had on the yard and the smell of fresh horse manure and leather was wonderful for a six year old girl.

My first memory is of remarking one day to Mr. Dooley that he must know everything about horses. As a six year old, I had obviously been pretty impressed! He just smiled and said that he didn't and in fact, no one knew everything about horses. I think that hearing this from someone I really respected at such a young age, impressed on me the fact that I could always learn something new from horses and that it was ok to question things and judge them for yourself, as no one had all the answers. Sometimes when there's a group of mixed age students, the younger lead rein students may be assigned to the most inexperienced teacher, as it can be assumed that young students aren't very demanding and won't need to be taught much. However, I think that if you teach children from the beginning how to have empathy for horses and to learn to question things and think for themselves, as much as how to sit in the saddle and look pretty, they will have a skill and understanding that will last them a lifetime. It's just like horses really. Great teachers create great students.

****

One of the strangest things I have noticed about horsemanship it is that the presence of a four legged equine seems to have an unnatural ability to cause normal human beings to stop thinking.

Instead, we often accept things at face value, because 'they've always been done that way,' or maybe because they were presented by someone you admire a lot. No one is always right. Even the person who runs a huge corporation, employing thousands of people in over a hundred counties around the world, sometimes gets things wrong. Amongst Taoisigh, presidents, teachers, trainers, including me, no one is always right. The only one that's always right is your equine student.

While I teach a little, I'm just a student like everyone else. As well as travelling out to Australia every few years to train with Brad, I try to go to as many other clinics and demos by other trainers as I can in Ireland and abroad, and I have more 'horsemanship' books than you can wave a stick at. Why? Because the more ideas I have, the more chances of success I have with horses. Often you might go in with a certain plan, but when plan A doesn't work, having alternative plans is invaluable.

****

I had been checking train times on the internet early one morning as I was due to go up to Dublin that afternoon, but somehow I ended up looking through various horse websites, and found something written about a young horse who had just been ridden for the first time.

174

From what was written, the horse had been fine with basic handling until the girth came out. He wasn't that comfortable when it tightened around him and was very ticklish under his stomach. He took off bucking and got the saddle off. The saddle was put on again straight away and according to the writer, the horse still looked uncomfortable, with fast shallow breathing and was being held tightly by the owner. Long-lines were introduced and when they touched the horses hind legs, the horse panicked again simply because he wasn't used to them. All this took about an hour, and when the horse was finally saddled a rider was brought out. For the rider to mount, the lead rope was held tightly by the trainer turning the horse's head around to its shoulder, to keep the horse in one place. On went the rider, took a few steps, the rider dismounted and that was it. The horse had been started. Allegedly. But that's not for me. I guess it was the opposite approach to what I was currently doing with Ozzie.

One of the things which stuck in my mind was something that Dad has always said. You've got to give your horse time. I agree and I would also add that as well as time, you've got to have an enjoyable easy training plan in place too. So you make it easy for your horse to learn, he enjoys it as much as you do and you let him do it in his own time.

The horse on the internet had an owner who was using a relatively kind training method. I've definitely heard of a lot worse. But what was missing from my point of view, was time, and being open to changing your plan if your horse is telling you he's not really comfortable with the situation. Usually when you're training a horse you can use your timeframe (i.e. you've got two minutes to get into the horsebox as we're late for the show) or your horse's timeframe (I'm not too sure about that saddle, can we go back and just try working with the numnah again?)

But how can you figure out what is your horse's time-frame? There's actually a very simple way. You look at your lead rope.

Generally if the lead rope is tight and you are often limiting your horse's movement (though there are a few exceptions) you are using your time. If the lead rope is usually loose, you are using your horse's time. It is 'loose rein thinking'. I believe that working in your horse's time is one of the most important aspects of training, particularly with a young horse.

So this morning, while I went out to catch Ozzie, I was thinking about this idea of loose rein training, and how it's not so important 'what' you teach your horse, but 'how' you teach your horse. If your young horse has all the basics done, including despooking and turning and stopping, and is used to saddles, girths, ropes, etc on the ground, you could put that horse into a paddock at home with no one watching, or into a demo situation with hundreds of people, and either way you'll still be sitting in the saddle in about five minutes.

I'd walked out to the field, and Ozzie was standing near the hedge maybe twenty steps away from me. I stopped to rearrange my halter and when I looked up Ozzie was half way over to me and still walking. A few seconds later he was standing right beside me. I gave him a rub and put on the halter, and led him in with a loose rope through the paddock into the round pen. As he stood there on a loose rein, we picked up all four feet and then put on the saddle, walked him around in a circle and then tightened the saddle securely. I asked Ozzie for lateral flexion, and after a hop or two I slowly lifted myself into the saddle from the far side. Then we stood there for about three minutes on a loose rein, Ozzie with a hindfoot resting, head down and ears relaxed with a strong wind blowing around us.

Soon we were doing nice figures of eight in walk with suppleness and bend. We stopped lightly when I raised the reins a little. We stood on a loose rein, and then I asked Ozzie for some hindquarter and forequarter yields, which he did with grace. I gave him a well deserved rub, and then I dismounted on the near side, took off his saddle, and led him back out on a loose rein to the field.

176

Granted this took about two months of work, and we had started with a horse who was a lot greener than the demonstration horse, yet the performances of the two horses couldn't have been father apart. Because I had taken the time (Ozzie's time!) to train Ozzie's mind as well as his body, I had ended up with a very happy, confident, secure and trusting little horse, who looked forward to his training sessions nearly as much as I did. Sometimes a little time goes a long way. It depends what kind of horse you want at the end of it.

29. Day eight in the saddle and improving my riding.

As I had spent so much time focusing on Ozzie, I thought it would be fun to focus on myself again for a weekend. So I had booked myself into a riding clinic up the north. To begin we had a talk about the importance of breathing. Slow deep breaths as you ride brings more oxygen around your body so you're less likely to be bouncing around like a tense brick on your horse's back. It's one of those things which doesn't sound all that important but which can actually have a huge effect on your horse. If you finish riding a jumping course or a dressage test and you're out of breath, then you weren't breathing much! Next up was balance and the shoulder-hip-heel idea. I'd done this years ago in pony camp, but while I'd nodded my head and accepted it, I'm not sure if I actually got it. One difficulty with this is that a lot of saddles have the stirrup bar attached too far forward, so it encourages your leg to be forward. So you can be riding around quite happily but sitting like you're in an armchair which makes the horse's job a bit more difficult. Alternatively, you can use lots of extra muscles in your legs to get your legs back, which is not really sustainable because you'll get tired faster than normal.

At one lesson there was a really nice English lady riding around, trying to concentrate on this shoulder-hip-heel line. At the time I was leading her horse around while she worked on this in the saddle. She was getting a bit frustrated.

The instructor shouted over some comments. 'Yes, just keep trying. If I took the horse away from underneath you now you'd land on your derriere. Your legs need to be back more.' The instructor was right but the English lady was getting frustrated. She was finding it physically very difficult to keep her lower legs further back.

When the trainer focused on someone else, she looked down at me and whispered: 'I think she thinks I'm a beginner! I've been riding in London for six years.'

She was getting a bit upset. I tried my best to reassure her she was doing fine.

'Listen, I don't think it's you at all, it's probably the saddle itself.' She peered down at me looking a bit distressed. I continued on.

'I'm not a very good rider or anything like that, but usually I try to look ahead, sit up straight and do the best I can. I was out in Australia a few years ago riding in an Australian stock saddle. When I was out there, there was a brilliant rider. She was working on level three stuff and it was just amazing to watch her and her horse. She was chatting to me during the week, and she remarked that I had a really nice seat, and said I must do a lot of dressage at home. I didn't! Basically the stock saddle put me in a nice position, and I just then tried my best to sit up straight and look ahead. You can only do your best though with what you've got.'

'Thanks Elaine. It's good to know there is hope!'

While the line from your shoulder-hip-heel had been in my head for over twenty years, I always just assumed I was doing it right. But I never checked against a mirror. I went home that evening, and stood sideways to a full length mirror. Then I bent my knees and kept my body straight as if I was in the saddle. When I did this, while I thought my heels were under my hips, they actually weren't! They were a bit forward. My upper body was being left behind also.

The next day I went back to the clinic. Even with the saddle putting my legs forward, I used some extra leg muscles and did a few laps with my legs back further than I would have them normally (my saddle has the stirrup bars too far forward as well). I felt a big difference. It felt more like I was floating along in balance with the horse.

So I guess it is one thing to know something, but it's another thing to get a bit particular about it and make sure you're doing it right.

At the clinic I was riding a green four year old. He had a lovely walk, good brakes and turning, and was light and sensitive. But I was having problems going from walk to trot. I was looking where I wanted to go, breathily deeply, had a good position and was using a small squeeze with my legs, but the horse just walked a bit faster, and didn't trot. Now of course I could have done something big – big leg squeeze, kick, really get energized, but I didn't want to. This horse was so willing I figured he wasn't trotting not because he didn't want to, but because he didn't understand my cues. So instead of making my confusing cues bigger, I needed to find a different cue that he'd understand.

There had been talk about imagining a circle of energy below your belly button. I hadn't really been getting the whole concept though. But as I walked on this little horse, I imagined that ball of energy in my seat was a Ryanair plane taking off down the runway. So my middle went forward, gathered speed and then took off up into the air. Within one stride of this visualization the horse broke into a lovely trot and trotted happily around the arena. I really do some strange things!

Another nice tip from this clinic was to ask a green horse to go from walk to trot for a few strides before they want to trot themselves. Often if you're riding in an arena your horse will have certain places where they like to speed up, and other places where they tend to slow down. When you want them to go back to walk, ask them to walk a few strides before the place where they normally start to slow down. You get the job done and you make it easy for the horse to do.

Over the past two weeks, between bad weather and doing lessons around the country Ozzie had been enjoying an early summer holiday. He had spent his days lying asleep in the grass, eating and growing, chasing cattle, chatting to the other two horses over the fence, and generally enjoying life as a horse of leisure. What I like to be able to do is catch a horse, pop on a saddle, hop on and go for a ride. But it was going to be a test as this was the longest I had ever gone without working Ozzie in some capacity. Would I be able to catch him? To tell you the truth I was just hoping I wouldn't have to report to work in Dublin with a broken bone and a story about a green horse. What I wanted to achieve was to repeat what we had done before and see how Ozzie behaved.

What happened later that day surprised me. I think sometimes that people who are new to horses or maybe look forward to their weekly lesson and the opportunity to be around these amazing creatures, have the right perspective – they want to develop a bond with their horse.

To them, the relationship they have with a horse is just as important to them as their ability to walk, trot and canter. I completely agree with them.

It's hard to imagine Ozzie used to be the scared horse that would bolt while being led beside a hedge (the dog used to mooch on the far side of it) or the little horse I spent three hours in the rain trying to attach the clip of the lead rope to his halter. He had come a long way. But still, while I thought that he always seemed to enjoy our training sessions, was easy to catch, always seemed relaxed and wouldn't rush off when let go, I still thought that he was just going along with things because it was something he 'had' to do, rather than something he 'chose' to do. I thought he behaved this way because I had trained him to be polite and easy to handle and not because he actually enjoyed our sessions as much as I did.

I was really looking forward to doing some work with him so I got my saddle and halter and headed down towards the round pen.

181

Arriving over at the fence, I put the saddle down on the grass and saw Ozzie watching me from the nearby field. I wandered over with a smile on my face, and after a few rubs and sniffs, the halter went on easily and we walked on. Dad had done tremendous work with the lawnmower and topper and now the whole paddock was again looking like a high quality golf course.

So he was simple to catch and lovely to lead. I picked up all four feet perfectly on loose rope in the arena, put on tack without a bother, got up, stood still with a loose rein, did some backup and hindquarter yields in halter, then spent a few minutes doing circles and figures of eight in walk. He was much better at changing directions, and understood that when I ask him to go it meant go until I asked him to stop, and not just to walk for a few steps. So we worked a bit on softness and flexion in walk, stood still, dismounted and gave him a huge rub. He was really coming on.

So I let him back into the field, and he stood there at the gate watching me go back to the house. As I moved away, he turned to face me directly. Then a second after I disappeared from view he whinnied after me!

It's amazing to think that a young horse who three months previously didn't want to be touched by a human was now whinnying when I went away. Definitely one of the best little horses around I reckoned. I had a huge smile on my face the whole way back up to Dublin.

30. Bolting over fences

'Houston, we have a big problem.'

It had been a gloriously sunny day in south Tipperary. A warm wind had been blowing through the fields and it was wonderful to feel the sunshine on my skin. It was the kind of day to sit on a chair outside with a cool drink and a good book. The dog was in top form, panting heavily in the heat, looking for someone to play with. Ozzie had been sighted earlier that morning lying down on the horizon, enjoying the unusually hot weather. We had done well over the last few weeks so the plan now was to introduce a pole on the ground and ask him to walk and trot gently over it. It sounded simple on paper anyway.

Ozzie could walk and trot nicely on a loose rope for a few circles either direction, and I knew from before that after a look or two, he was fine walking over a pole on the ground, forwards and backwards.

I asked him to walk in a circle, and as he came round I positioned him so he'd have to walk over the pole on a loose rein. No bother at all. He was relaxed and happy, walked over the pole a few times, so I gave him a rub and a rest as a thank you.

At this stage, with no issues moving nicely over the pole in walk, it was time to make the circle a little bigger and ask him to trot slowly around, including a nice trot over the pole.

As in walk, I was looking for a nice relaxed movement over the pole, as if the pole wasn't even there. If I knew he could do a pole on the ground well, then I could start thinking about doing the same in the saddle, working up towards trotting nicely over a few cross poles at the end of the summer. At the minute I just wanted to build really good simple foundations. And this is where things started to go wrong.

183

I asked Ozzie to walk over the pole again, which was fine. Then I asked him softly to trot. He broke into a nice trot, but once he came back around towards the pole, he began to panic and speed up.

One lap later he was still speeding up, and was now doing a defensive worried canter. He kept getting faster and more panicked. I stood in the middle of the circle, completely still, watching. Ozzie was going so fast, in a very small circle and he was starting to tilt inwards, dangerously close to falling over sideways. And this was just a pole on the ground, not even a jump!

I asked him to stop, and he came back into me immediately, stressed and trembling and I spent a minute or two calming him down. My mind was racing.

'Oh no,' I thought. 'This is a problem. I own a horse who bolts over fences. How on earth am I going to fix this?'

I stood there with Ozzie and thought about it for a few minutes.

When he started getting faster, my first plan was just to let him do what he wanted and when I started to see him slow down, I'd ask him to stop altogether. The idea being that he'd understand I wanted him to go over the fence slowly and not like a rocket-ship.

The problem with that plan was that he wasn't getting any slower, and it was getting a bit dangerous. So I needed another plan.

Because Ozzie was polite and mannerly in every other respect, this wasn't due to dominant behaviour. He was also happy walking and backing over poles, so it wasn't because Ozzie was scared of poles.

It wasn't because of anything a rider was doing, because there was no rider onboard. The interesting part was that he was perfect walking over the pole, but only panicked when asked to trot or canter over it.

He wasn't bolting over fences because he was sore or a bad jumper or spooky or bolshy. I suspected he was bolting over fences because it was very likely his last owners had taught him to.

Ireland isn't that well known for its dressage, but it is renowned for its showjumping and cross country horses. Young horses that jump well (and for some people that means high) can sell for a lot of money. So there's a huge focus on jumping young unbroken horses over large fences, so a potential buyer can see how well they jump.

Sometimes this can go a bit wrong, and the focus is put on how high the horse can jump, rather than how well he can jump. And to clear a high jump, you'd want a good fast canter into it, particularly if it was a really high jump.

It is not unusual to see little horses trying to jump big fences at a flat out gallop at the sales. It's a bit like watching car-crash television sometimes. To be honest, up to this stage Ozzie hadn't really shown me anything he'd been taught previously, aside from disliking people, so I guess the previous owner spent a little time turning Ozzie from a wild four year old into a jumping rocket.

I didn't want to own an uncontrollable rocket though. Rockets don't jump over fences. They tend to blast straight through them.

'Hhhmm,' I thought. 'I'll need to come up with a plan to fix this.'

****

Ozzie needed some retraining. He assumed that I wanted him to gallop over jumps. So that was what he was doing.

What I needed was some way to explain to Ozzie when he started to get fast that I actually wanted him to slow down again. I thought back to my days spent teaching young riders to jump and to give them confidence for their first few jumps, and to keep them safe and onboard. To the delight of the nervous riders I used to jog over the jump a few times with them. Once they had got their seat and steering in order I'd pretend to collapse, smile and say I'd done my best and they were on their own now. Then I'd stand in a strategic position whenever the ponies tended to cut corners, and watch the progress from there. It worked a treat.

The other instructors thought I was crazy and that I did too much for the children, but I ended up with confident riders, who had courage and good seats and the important safety net present early on. It was also a good way to warm yourself up on a cold day.

So I started to wonder could I help my horse over the pole like I had helped those young riders over the fences? Could I keep him safe, build his confidence, and be right there with him explaining exactly what I wanted him to do? I reckoned it was worth a shot.

A while back another horse person made a throwaway comment about how big an impact unexpectedly ending a training session can be for a horse. That comment had stuck in my head and I was going to put it to the test.

****

Later on I caught Ozzie and brought him over to the pole in the centre of the paddock. He had a sniff and a nibble, and then caught it in his mouth and lifted one end of it up into the air. He wasn't scared of it anyway which was good. I got him walking over it on a loose rein, and he was fine again.

After a few minutes of this I started to increase my energy a little, hoping to get a more energetic walk out of him. This he did. But when he started to worry that I wanted him to trot, he would speed up straight away into a few bouncy canter strides.

Firstly, I was only going to ask him to go over the fence once.

When his energy levels went up, I brought mine down.

Horses do tend to mirror your energy so I hoped it would help to reassure him that I didn't want him to do the speed stakes. Every time he walked calmly over the fence, he got a rest and a rub and his energy levels lowered again.

I wanted to work on his mind, because if I could lower his anxiety and worry, his body would slow down too. So we alternated between nice calm walks over the pole, to canter bounces when I fractionally increased my energy. The whole time I worked on lowering his energy and giving him confidence.

Ozzie had been trained so well to do it wrong, it was going to take a while to train him how to do it right and not to automatically panic. After about twenty minutes, he had calmed down overall again, and the bouncy canter was getting less frequent. It was still all a bit messy though.

What I was looking for was any kind of movement that resembled a slow easy trot over the pole. We did a few more passes over the pole at walk and I raised my energy a fraction.

Just before the pole, Ozzie broke into a slow bouncy elevated trot, trotted over it like an Arabian on a loose rope, and then stopped quietly when I asked him to. No canter bounces no rushing off, no panic.

Bingo.

I undid the halter, took it off him in one action and immediately stepped away from him, all in about two seconds as a reward for trotting the first time over the pole without panicked forward movement. He looked at me as if to say 'was that it?'

Then he wandered off, ate a few blades of grass and then took off at a gallop with his tail high up to the top of the paddock where Pepsi had been watching.

187

What beautiful elevated movement over the pole that last time in trot! It wasn't too far off the passages I had seen the previous weekend in the Spanish riding school in a sun drenched Jerez de la Frontera. With potential and movement like that, I could have a talented dressage horse as well as a speed stakes showjumper on my hands! It was a good training session. Over that weekend we did three or four more sessions like this. Every time I got slightly less panic, I would stop him, take all the tack off him as quickly as I could and within seconds he was completely free. Hopefully he would ponder over it for the week until I saw him again.

****

Next weekend I was back down from Dublin. Top of my list, along with some riding, was to practise our slow jumping again.

Originally Ozzie's four biggest issues were that he:

- Didn't like to be touched
- Was impossible to catch
- Wouldn't let his feet be picked up
- Bolted over fences

Saturday was a soft day. Light rain had been falling from the higher clouds all morning and when it stopped just before lunch, I put on my coat, muckers and gloves and headed out to Ozzie to see how his trot over a pole would be.

To be honest I wasn't expecting much.

He had shown a fair bit of panic when I asked him to trot quietly over a pole last weekend, so I was ready to offer lots of confidence, reassurance, and patience, while I waited for Ozzie to do the one easy trot over the pole which I was looking for. I had already done about three sessions that weekend, so he had been gradually improving during each one.

I went out, ducked under the fence into the paddock, and headed over towards the pole. Ozzie spotted me immediately and walked with me as I headed towards the far side of the paddock. We did like each other's company.

I changed the pole to a different position to the previous week, and then haltered Ozzie. A few rubs and we were off. Oz was chilled out and relaxed and each time I asked him, he walked beautifully over the pole, stopping after each attempt for me to tell him how wonderful and brave I thought he was.

We did this about five times, so the next time I asked him to walk again, I started to increase my energy a little and added a few vocal clicks to give him a cue that I wanted him to increase the pace a little. His walk became a little more forward moving, and again he walked nicely over the pole. I asked him to stop a few steps later and in he came for more rubs and praise. I was still looking for that trot though.

A minute later and I asked him again to circle around me on a loose rope, and as he moved around I cued him into a light trot. This was about his seventh time going over the pole this morning, and only about four or five minutes into our lesson. He picked up an easy trot, trotted over the pole loosely, continued on for a few strides afterwards and then I asked him to stop. He did so immediately, and came back into me for rubs and praise.

We had done it!!!!!!! What had taken the bones of forty-five minutes the previous weekend had now taken five minutes. Within seconds I had taken off his halter, gave him a quick rub and stepped away from him, walking back rapidly towards the house.

He looked at me with a puzzled expression on his face.

'Hey you! Come back over here!!!'

The fruitcake, now loose, immediately started to follow me up the paddock. I stood and waited for him to walk up to me. I gave him lots of rubs and praise as he stood beside me with a big grin on his face. I was so proud of him.

There were still a few more weeks work to do on this, but because of my actions, Ozzie had started to realise than unlike his previous trainers, I just wanted him to move slowly and confidently over a fence, and that he didn't need to panic or worry anymore.

I was so happy I came back in and cooked dinner for everyone which raised more than a few eyebrows!

31. Our first trot

I had been fairly busy over the previous few weeks up in Dublin. Most of our I.T. issues in work had been sorted out and so all was proceeding calmly, servers and storage systems alike.

I had been doing some horses as well so the upshot of all of this was that for the previous few months, I had only been down to Tipperary five or six times.

With hindsight, it's probably best not to start a young horse on a part-time basis. I had been lucky that I lived at home for the first few months, but now that I lived three hours away progress had got pretty slow. I found that when I went home our time on Saturday was spent doing a recap of what we had done the previous weekend – both for Ozzie and me to remember and then on Sunday we'd try to do something new.

So for every weekend I did make it home I only really had one session where we progressed a little. The joys of working in Dublin.

Anyway, after my escapades around Dublin it was time to take the Cork road and head down to Tipperary. I decided to do so in style, booked Friday off work and drove down on Thursday night. Our wood burner had been installed into the lounge the previous day, so the lounge was warm and covered in dust and soot.

Early on Friday morning I put on my worst clothes and armed with Pledge all purpose polish and a mountain of kitchen towels, I cleaned my way around the room, and brandished a hoover dangerously in the same area as a fitting finale. After that exertion, it was into Tipperary for the paper run. Unfortunately I was delayed and ended up in both centres of podiatry wear. In my own defence I must admit I am quite talented at choosing stunning shoes, but unfortunately I am not quite as adept at balancing in them.

Thus after a late lunch on Friday, I was already worn out and retired gracefully to the lounge to bask in front of the wood burner, which was performing nicely.

Soon three o'clock had somehow turned into six o'clock and food had to be organised before Ireland played France in the World Cup. Back in the lounge I spent the next two hours watching Ireland being annihilated by a superb French side, who spotted every Irish mistake and then drove a whole army of French men through all of them. It looked like I'd be doing Ozzie on Saturday.

****

Since the middle of the previous week, winter had introduced itself and the nights had become quite cold. It had started to rain a lot. It was the time of year when a flight to Australia started to look very appealing. On Saturday we had a brief respite and after a chilly start, the sun came out and the afternoon turned out quite warm. After my quiet day the previous day, I was rested and full of ideas. I wanted to work towards getting Ozzie to pop over a pole loose and to do our first trot together.

Dad headed down the farm on the quad to meet the slurry man, and I put a jump into the round pen while Ozzie walked over towards me. He had a nose in everything. I caught him, opened the wire and led him down to the round pen. I put on the saddle while he stood on a loose rein, and then I took off his halter and asked him to circle me in a walk and trot in both directions as the stirrups flapped around him. No bother.

I brought in the two blocks and the pole and Ozzie was straight over, trying his best to help by rearranging everything with his teeth and feet. With the pole on the ground, I got him to walk and then trot over it both ways. He happily walked and trotted over it, stopped after it, did a forequarter yield on a cent and then popped over it again the opposite way. I reckoned if he could do that then maybe we could try a slight bigger jump.

So up went the white blocks and the black plastic pole was soon rested on top of them. Ozzie was in his element. He did lovely trots over the fence in both directions, with absolutely no sign of rushing, panic or worry whatsoever. Once you directed him near the jump, he'd automatically position himself so that he ended up going over it nicely. I think I can confidently say that our 'rushing at fences' problem was officially history, touch wood.

Dad had arrived back in the meantime, so just for fun he asked Ozzie to circle around him loose in a walk, trot and canter on both reins. It was a textbook performance with some nice flexion and softness, and Ozzie came straight into Dad the second he was cued and then stuck to him like glue. It was a pity I didn't have a camera.

We did our feet picking out ritual and on I hopped. I made a point of making Ozzie walk strongly around the arena and we ended up with a lovely soft forward moving walk in both directions, with the lightest of brakes, good hindquarter yields and perfect light turning both right and left.

As we walked around, I started to move my seat bones a little faster than the movement of the saddle. Ozzie picked up on this and walked on a little more. As we came past the gate, I did this again, squeezed a little with my legs for a split second and asked him on with my voice, giving him room with the reins to move forward. For the first few times he wasn't too sure what I wanted and just increased the pace, but then as we headed north east he broke into a few steps of trot.

It was without doubt the most enjoyable trot I'd ever sat to.

We continued to walk on, and then a few laps later I asked again. Sure enough, Ozzie broke into another nice easy trot. As with the walk, I first wanted to teach him how to move into a trot, and once he got this, I'd follow-up by teaching him to stay in a trot.

But one step at a time.

193

We came back to a walk, walked another circle or two, and then I turned him to a stop. The grin on my face was only surpassed by the grin on Ozzie's. I was really proud of him.

32. Bucked off.

In August, roughly six months after I bought Ozzie at the sales, he was really a different horse. He was much more confident and trusting and he wasn't spooky any more. He could do all the basic horse things and he could be ridden nicely at a walk and trot in a halter. He had good brakes, a good attitude and while I still knew he could be a handful every now and again, I was pretty pleased with him.

I posted the beginning of Ozzie's story on an online equestrian group, along with a few pictures of him looking relaxed and confident to see what others thought of how Ozzie and I had been getting on. I got a few replies.

"Goodness what a good story! And what a lovely horse"

"Almost forgot this was a real life story for a moment. He is gorgeous, no wonder you fell for him."

"This is such a fantastic thread. Ozzie is a really super wee horse isn't he? Can utterly see why you went for him."

Bloody hell! Ozzie may have been a looker but he was also a pretty tough nut to crack. He was very reactionary and came with a motley collection of well developed opinions he didn't like to let go of. I replied as truthfully as I could.

"That's the thing though, he is not super. He is actually a pain in the backside! He's clever, he doesn't like me to contradict myself at all, is very sensitive to the touch, stubborn and has a rogue-ish glint in his eye (perhaps the camera didn't catch the glint!). You could never wear him out (tough as old boots was one description!) He actually took longer to bring on than I expected - if there was a tiny gap in my teachings, he'd be straight out through it.

I think probably some of the most useful things to bring to your horse are a few basic principles in your back pocket. My main ones were that we'd always go at Ozzie's speed, and that I wanted him to mentally accept everything we did together - so lots of stuff was done on a loose rein. After that, time, the patience of a saint, practise and a good few horsey friends to chat about things with and get ideas and support from can make a huge difference."

One lady hit the nail on the head.

"Lovely El, I've really enjoyed reading Ozzie's story. I have a funny little horse with a similar background. It's been so rewarding having her in my life, and things are certainly never dull as I'm sure she spends most of her time thinking of new challenges she can set me! That's what came across to me from Ozzie's story. That there's so much learning that happens on both side of the horse - human partnership. Having young horses could become addictive, it's such a gift being able to watch them grow and learn, I'm loving it."

In hindsight what I had actually done by the end of the summer was to get through the first couple of layers with Ozzie. But there were a lot of layers I hadn't even scratched yet. In those six months he had changed from being untouchable, uncatchable and un-rideable to doing a lot of the basic handling and riding tasks. The trouble was I had actually bought a lot of horse for my money - more than I had initially realised.

I was at home for the weekend at the end of August and my brother Jonathan was also about. He is about six foot two inches of tall white Irishness. On this particular Saturday afternoon there was a rugby match on. Once it finished Dad and I traipsed out to do a session with Ozzie and Jonathan disappeared off to change into his running gear for a jog around the farm. I got the saddle and halter and my hat and headed out to catch Ozzie, and soon enough was riding at in a nice walk as Dad watched on.

Soon Jonathan appeared out and proceeded to bound long-legged up the big paddock. Ozzie looked on in disbelief. He had never seen a 'Jonathan' before. Jonathan disappeared over the horizon and I continued working with Ozzie.

Every so often Jonathan would appear over a far ditch like an unearthly figure bounding across the horizon. Ozzie would see him immediately and stop and stare with his eyes on stalks. Every time I cued him to walk on again. This all went fine for the first few times. Then it happened again.

Ozzie saw Jonathan once more and stopped dead. I cued him to walk on. He thought 'bugger that' and then did a really spectacular bronc. The whole horse went up and twisted at the same time. It was as clear a 'feck off' as you could probably get from a horse. I went flying and landed on my back wheezing at the far side of the arena. I lay there for a few seconds not quite believing what had just happened. Dad rushed over and knelt beside me as I tried to raise my head up to see how Ozzie was.

'Lord, are you ok Elaine?' Dad looked worriedly down at me as I struggled to catch my breath. I was grand, just a bit winded.

Ozzie was at the far side of the round pen wondering what I was doing on the ground and looked a bit unsure of himself.

'I'm fine, just catch Ozzie,' I wheezed. So Dad went over and caught Oz. After about ten seconds I got up and walked unsoundly over to Oz and gave him a gentle rub on his nose.

'That wasn't really in the plan buddy,' I said to him.

My bloody back hurt. Ouch. I got back up on Ozzie and walked a lap or two around the arena, gave him a rub and then got off.

I had made a mistake somewhere along the line and now it had come back to bite me. I couldn't believe that even after all the work I had a horse who could still pull a stunt like this on me. I really thought we'd sorted out any leadership issues we had had.

For the next few months I continued riding Ozzie, but made sure Jonathan wasn't going jogging at the same time. Nothing else of note happened but in the back of my mind I knew there was an issue there which we needed to figure out. I just didn't have the answer yet. I was worried and de-motivated, I have to admit.

After doing Ozzie solidly for the six months I needed a bit of a break to think about what we'd achieved, as well as to recharge my batteries. In fact maybe both of us needed some time off. In late October I left Ozzie off for the winter and headed back up to Dublin to what was becoming a very wet and cold winter in Ireland.

33. Christmas.

Soon it was Christmas and after a few parties up in Dublin and a fair bit of shopping in Liffey Valley, the Omnipark and another shopping centre up near the airport I arrived down to Tipperary laden down with presents. I was deliriously glad to have a week stretching before me of doing as little as possible with the exception of eating, sleeping, vegetable preparation and washing up.

My two brothers and my sister arrived down soon after in their various cars. We had done a family swop a few months previously, so I now had Dad's jeep, Lauren had my little car, Jonathan had Mum's car, and Mum and Dad had got new cars, so there were cars everywhere. It's funny how families go through stages. Twenty years ago it had been toy cars, pony stuff and transformers everywhere. On Christmas Eve I had all my presents parceled up and Dad and myself were hanging around inside.

'Hey Dad...' I looked over at him.

'Yes?' he replied.

'I was thinking I might pop out and catch Ozzie. What do you think?' This was code for 'will you come out as well please and give me some advice.'

'Sure why not?'

'Excellent!' I smiled.

So out I went, caught Ozzie, brought him into the round pen, threw on the saddle and halter and sat up on him for the first time in two months. We walked about, stopped, reversed, turned, did a few yields and messed about a bit. He was perfect. There was not an argument in sight. Maybe that buck a few months back had just been a blip. I gave him a rub, got off, let him off again and he wandered away happily.

On Christmas day we went to Mass at ten, had coffee at eleven thirty and then headed down to the drawing room to open the presents. By 3pm we had done a good job on both the turkey and the pudding and were feeling happily fat and sleepy. Dad and I headed out and I caught Ozzie, wished him a happy Christmas, put on the tack and I got into the saddle as Dad watched. We did the same as on Christmas eve and while Ozzie did everything fine, I could feel the start of a few 'I don't want to's'. Nothing big mind you. Just the impression that while the previous day I felt in complete control, today it wasn't quite 100%. Maybe just 99%. Hmm I thought. As Gerry Adams once said 'we haven't gone away you know'. Ozzie hadn't gone away either. There was still an underlying issue.

I let him go again and walked back into the house. I needed to come up with a plan to get to the inner horse and get past this slight 'unpredictability/argumentative' issue. The weather was pretty awful for the rest of the Christmas so I didn't do any more with Ozzie. Soon I was back working in Dublin.

My plan was to start work again with Ozzie the following spring and tackle this issue right from the start. Up in Dublin I worked away publishing and sorting out encoding failures and film festival launches. As January turned into February, and then March I checked the weather for each weekend. It rained solidly for nearly all of them. It was hopeless horse weather. March turned into April, which also rained solidly and before I knew it, it was June. It was time to come up with a definite plan and get back in the saddle.

34. Creating a plan.

I was on the internet again so I posted up my dilemma on an American discussion group to get a few opinions.

"This is about my six year old horse. I would appreciate any thoughts.

Last year I bought Ozzie and restarted him. As I was living down in Tipperary at the time, I did a lot of groundwork with him for the first three months - trust, confidence, manners, leadership. All you could do with him at the start was lead him - he'd go to the far side of the stable when he saw you coming, was hard to catch, I couldn't touch him, couldn't put on a headcollar, he didn't like humans and was very spooky. He had no trust or confidence.

Then I moved back up to Dublin, and came down every weekend or two and got him backed and riding nicely and softly in a walk and trot in our round pen.

The nervousness had mostly gone though he was still super sensitive, and he proved that you really had got to have your wits about you as he took what I said literally and learned faster than I do. I left him out over the winter, and rode him a few times over Christmas. I was going to bring him back in the spring, but due to the rotten weather over here and being in Dublin most weekends, I'm just starting this now.

Most times he's fine but once every few weeks/blue moon he'll just say no and argue with me. He's not a pushover horse. So there are two main areas I want to work on. First is handling. I know I need to do more to really desensitise him to me. This would also hopefully get rid of the occasional odd 'ears back grumpy look' too.

Secondly - he's perfect loose in a round pen with directions and gait and stopping. The only thing he finds difficult to do is when he's in a big paddock with a halter on and I ask him to circle. If he decides 'no' (usually in trot) and pulls away from me, then feels the halter stopping him from going away further he can throw a bit of a strop against this pressure on his head. So I thought that'd be a good one to work on too.

So here is my question. It was the first time I'd ridden him since Christmas so he was super with the tack and getting up and standing, but I was a bit disheartened when the 'no' came back again when he got distracted by something and I could feel that coiled spring underneath me... do you have any suggestions of ideas on how to get help resolve this?"

I got a few answers.

"I know what that feels like! I've got a mare that sounds like your guy! Every once in a while that spring would "bust loose" and she'd try like heck to buck me off! I didn't know how to deal with it until last summer! So, this is what I do, it seems to help focus her attention and relax that spring!

When she starts to "coil up" (I really like how you described it - it's exactly how it feels!!), I do serpentines until I can feel her relax. Once she realizes that it's harder to work on that exercise rather than behave like a lady, she's calmed down enough to continue with our lesson.

Also, with the 'no', I worked on the 'go' switch. She moves when I want her to move and asks questions later! It's almost like you have to push them through the little tantrum by making them use more energy and then they realize that when you give them the opportunity to stop and rest, they really appreciate it. My mare would do the 'no' thing on the trail. So, when we first started working on this problem, I'd get off and go back to groundwork. It's as if I had to say to her "This is forward, this is stop . . . remember? You need to pay attention to me and not everything else around you". *Loved reading through your log. It might be long, but it's a quick read!"*

****

"He is a very handsome lad!! I've found that my horses may be totally OK with something when I'm on the ground but startle when I'm riding them. I would say it certainly wouldn't hurt to do the in-hand work, but if you feel brave and confident, continue working from the saddle and just disengage the hindquarters when you feel the spring coiling. I'm lucky that 99% of the time if something startles my horses they will jump and "plant" - then they just stare at what startled them."

****

"He is just so darn CUTE!"

Giving Ozzie a job to do immediately when he zoned out on me was a very good point. Disengaging the hindquarters when I felt him coil up should help to stop him doing a bronc. I also wanted to get back into a good bit of groundwork and continue on with what I had been doing last year. Met Eireann predicted that a less than normal amount of rain was due to fall the following weekend, so I booked Thursday and Friday off work and drove home to do some work with my horse.

35. Groundwork – revisiting the basics.

'Feck it, would you ever stop hugging me!' Ozzie pleaded earnestly.

'Sorry buddy,' I replied solemnly. 'You are just going to have to get used to it.'

The plan for the weekend was to spend most of it with Ozzie. On Thursday morning I decided Ozzie was going to get really used to me, so I caught him and then calmly proceed to hug the life out of him for about fifteen minutes. If anyone had seen me they would have thought I was totally bananas. After a while he was like 'yeah, whatever, ok I give up. You're mad.' He was totally relaxed. Then I spent about twenty minutes detangling his tail as he stood half asleep in the sun on a loose rope. Then I picked up all his feet. Not a bad start after five months, I thought.

On Thursday evening he was a bit more awake. When I went out himself and Dougal were galloping about play fighting with each other, and tearing from one end of the paddock to the other. I caught him and did some leading.

Every now and again I would get an 'I won't' so I just let him do his thing then repeated my request for him to walk on. It was the same 'I won't' as the one last summer. Then on went the numnah and saddle, and I made as much of a mess of it as I could. The numnah was being thrown on from all directions and the saddle was making a hell of a lot of noise but Ozzie stood half asleep on a loose rope as if he'd seen this hundreds of times before. Then it was back to some one line work in the big paddock. We did walk and trot in a circle on the rope, and he threw a few wobblies in trot when he felt pressure on the halter after he'd tried to pull away from me and go off somewhere else. I didn't pull, I just didn't go with him. He got over it when he realised I wasn't one to be pulled around and I got some nice work out of him on both reins. This was great though. I had found my arguments and I had found a safe way to work with Ozzie and get past them.

Friday was spent doing more of the same. I did two sessions with him in the morning, focusing mainly on circling in walk, trot and canter without arguments. If I got any arguments I would just repeat my cue to walk on until Ozzie gave up and went, 'ok fine I'll just walk on'.

There were a few wobblies in the second session, so I decided Ozzie was going to have the pleasure of another short session that evening. When I went out he was bombing around after Dougal, play acting and doing his best to bite Dougal's derriere. I caught him and then got some really nice work on both reins - not a wobbley in sight!

The difference in this session was that even though there was still the odd head shake, there was also absolutely no pressure from him on the lead rope - even when he shook his head, he'd do it in such a way as to not pull against his halter. I think in the thirty minutes he pulled on the lead rope a little twice - and only in a small way. It was a great session, particularly as it had started to rain half way through it but it was worth damp clothes. Was I starting to get through to the inner horse?

Saturday was a beautiful day. The sun was back out and Ozzie was up at the top of the paddock. I went up and caught him, led him around on a loose rope and did about three circles on both reins in trot, in between walking about.

He was perfect. There were no arguments and some nice softness. Once or twice he got distracted and looked over where Dad was putting handles on wire, but then he focused again on the job in hand when I asked him to. It was probably time to start upping the 'distraction' factor which traditionally made Ozzie stop listening and zone out... so first I got the dog out, put Ozzie in a new paddock, and then some church bells rang on cue which was all fine. I went into Tipperary later on and bought him a mineral block so he spent the rest of the evening trying his best to demolish it.

That Saturday I gave the poor horse another hug. I was sure he was fed up with me at that stage. I put on his halter, did some easy circles in walk and trot and it was all very chilled. I brought out a pole, and Ozzie did an easy walk over it both ways and a perfect trot over it too. Then I raised it up a little and again he did a nice easy walk and trot. He was so relaxed he was actually quite intent on demolishing/playing/eating it. I was quite chuffed he remembered all the retraining work we did last year with the bolting over jumps issue.

Anyway I let him go and he played with the pole for a while, then he cantered back over and stuck his head back in his mineral block. Later on I looked out and a bullock had somehow managed to jump into Ozzie's paddock. Ozzie didn't look very bothered. Ten minutes later I looked back out and Ozzie was chasing him about at a good canter. The poor bullock looked petrified. After a while the unfortunate bovine had had enough of the mad grey horse and took the wire fence at speed, jumped over it cleanly and galloped across the next field putting as much distance as he could between himself and Ozzie. Ozzie, now satisfied the world was fine again went back to eating grass.

On Saturday evening I thought it was time to add in a little chaos.

I parked my jeep out in front of the house and turned up the radio full volume (90's dance anthems). Then I brought my brother out who was wearing a questionable red jacket and asked him politely to run / hop / star jump / clap up at the top of the paddock as I worked Ozzie. He gave me a funny look but agreed to the plan under the condition there would be no visual footage recorded of any of this.

With the radio blaring and the brother doing a mentaller at the top end of the paddock, I asked Ozzie to do a bit of circling in walk and trot. While he was a bit concerned about Jonathan, he did his work and he was brave and did everything I asked without any arguments. I was quite proud of him in fact. Jonathan also got a great workout and disappeared in after about fifteen minutes with a big red face on him.

Later on, I brought him into the yard for a well deserved wander and an apple. When Ozzie was coming out, he got a bit of a fright (a deadly horse-eating bird in a bush) and rushed forward. The split second Ozzie felt pressure from me on the lead rope to slow down, he did straight away. Things were slowly coming together.

Finally, I decided to take things easy again and get my brother back out in a less scary coat and let Ozzie make friends with him.

On Sunday morning I walked Ozzie in and out of the windy yard, beside the jeep and over the hose pipes, found him an apple which he ate while keeping an eye on the dog who was tearing about, and then led him back out through the spooky lane which lived up to its name. Out in the paddock, I got Jonathan to make a quiet appearance. Ozzie spotted him straightaway and was happy to wander over to him. After a fair bit of sniffing, Ozzie was on to the friendly nibble stage. Jonathan had passed the Oz-test so we left it there. It was all just handling and putting hours on the clock. I really wished I was home more often.

For our tenth training session that weekend I circled Ozzie both ways. I brought him into the round pen and he got a bit spooked in there. It was pretty windy, situated right next to the trees and hedges. I circled him again and soon his energy levels came down a bit and he started to focus on the work.

I tacked up, hopped on and then sat up there doing nothing. Ozzie had not a bother in the world and was very accepting of all of this. I rode around at a walk. He did a few spooks but I didn't mind those. He was nice and relaxed so I ended it there. This was the second time he'd had a saddle on, and the first time I'd ridden him since Christmas, so it was good.

Chatting to Dad later on I was pretty pleased.

'He's coming on well now. Sometimes I think it's a pity he's not a bit bigger.'

Dad looked across at me with a wry expression.

'He's big enough!'

36. Getting rid of the no's when riding.

During the week as June turned into July and it continued to pour rain in Dublin, Dad had done a session in my absence. Ozzie was led around the yard for an hour in the wind with dogs and cattle galloping around. There was the odd leading argument but Ozzie got over it. After that, Ozzie did a bit of circling followed by a trot over a small pole, then a trot over a small log then a jump over a big log in the paddock. He was quite a stylish jumper I was told.

I drove home on Saturday and I had my lateral flexion and hindquarter yields in place for the 'no's' during riding. I caught Ozzie then worked for a few minutes on getting a bit of softness through his body in walk and trot on both reins. Dad took over, repeated the same exercises and then walked and popped Ozzie over the pole and log again.

We brought him into the round pen, tacked him up and trotted him around loose while he jumped and spooked at stuff.

'He's a bit spooky alright,' Dad said conversationally. 'Maybe for today you should just get up and get off again. The ground is a bit hard at the minute.'

I'm fairly stubborn when I want to be. At that stage I'd spent since Christmas thinking about exactly what I needed to do, so I was keen to get up there and get the job started.

'No. At this stage I think it's time to just push through this and get the job done. I'll turn him quick if I feel him getting wound up and we'll see how we get on. If it all turns to custard well then fair enough we'll have to think of something else.'

I mounted up and Ozzie and I hopped and spooked our way a bit around the circle on both reins. When Ozzie was relaxed and soft then so was I. When he spooked I ignored it. When he looked outside the pen, I immediately asked him to look back in with my inside rein. When Ozzie got tense, I asked him straight away for lateral flexion at a halt and held it until I got softness - usually about five to eight seconds later. So off we walked again straightaway. I knew Ozzie could do all this stuff nicely, so it was now time for him to do the job and stop faffing about.

The more we did the better we got. I was actually looking forward to the "no's" for my instant lateral flexion demo. As we kept doing circle after circle, each of his actions was met by a predictable response from me. At the end he was actually quite chilled as we walked around, with lots of yawning going on. It was really good actually.

The next morning was very windy and Ozzie was hopping all over the place. I circled him on the ground both ways at walk/trot/canter and again at the start he wasn't listening. He was too focused on all the exciting stuff the wind was blowing about, but he calmed down after a while. I tacked him up and hopped on. As we walked around there were lots of jumps and a few 'no's again. I ignored the jumps, relaxed and got soft when he did, and when I got the 'what is over there is too interesting, I'm not listening to you anymore' I went straight into lateral flexion and held it till I got softness.

It was pretty windy with branches cracking, so we did pretty well. At one stage I had got about three nice circles in walk out of him and I was just thinking........ maybe that's a good place to stop?

As I said it out loud, Oz started his 'no's' again, so I had to deal with those with more lateral flexion, reminding him 'go' doesn't mean stand still. We ended on a good note. There were no real 'I won't's' Spooks and jumps yes, a few 'I'm not moving I'll just ignore you' (but he did move), but nothing that serious. When his mind wandered I picked up my inside rein to ask him to come back to me again.

I reckoned it was a case of repetition. I just needed to keep answering all the questions he asked until he figured out this deal was here for good. It was useful to do this stuff with lots of distractions. I knew that if it was a calm day, he'd probably toddle around fine and I'd get further but in the long run it wouldn't have taught him that much.

It was a good weekend's work. Sometimes you realise it's quite a responsibility to bring on a young horse. You really don't want to mess them up.

37. An Australian in England

The more I worked with Ozzie the more I reckoned I needed to learn. That summer I took advantage of the woeful weather in Ireland (there were floods in August!), to go over to England again and watch some more good trainers.

I picked up a sparkling clean black Vauxhall Astra at Gatwick airport, and proceeded to get it as muddy as I could. It was a little dinger of a car. I recognised a few faces from my last trip to Tunbridge Wells, so the first morning started off happily with a short discussion among the participants. The main things they wanted to work on were confidence, softness and leadership.

The trainer was an extremely tall Australian who actually sounded a little more English than Australian. I'm used to my Australians sounding Australian! Five horses were brought into the outdoor arena, so predictably as they were in a new place with new neighbours, they all had their heads and energy levels up. There was a beautiful huge coloured horse, the cutest small chestnut you've ever seen with a white splash across his face, a small bay horse, a big bay horse and a small chestnut horse.

It would make sense that the best way to settle horses that are prancing about and looking at everything is to be very quiet and relaxed yourself. In practise however if a horse's blood is up they can tend to ignore you if you stay passive. The idea was for the human to create even more energy. Kind of along the lines of 'so you think that stuff out there is interesting? Hell, take a look at the crazy stuff I'm doing in here!'

All the horses were in halters and twelve foot ropes and each human had a long stick with a rope tied onto the end of it. Basically the idea was to stand in front of your horse and slowly get your horse used to the stick being waved energetically about. At the start the horses weren't 100% about this, so the sticks were going quite slowly. In some cases to make it easier for the horses, folks would lead the horse so he was following the stick (in horse terms chasing the stick away). After a while of this, the horses started to get their focus back in on their handlers and by the end there was some pretty impressive high energy work going on with sticks being waved pretty fast in all directions and the horses nice and relaxed while all this commotion was going on. One idea which was brought up was that if you wanted your horse to be 100% solid and confident when he is out hacking or at a show, then you are going to need him to be 300% solid and confident when he's at home, so doing work like this really helps. Each time you get through this, you and your horse will have lived through another catastrophe, and you are increasing your horses confidence in you all the time.

Ideally if you're good at this you can have your horse completely loose and you can then walk around him in a circle waving sticks and ropes like a lunatic and he won't blink an eyelid.

The trainer said the first time he brought on a horse it took him fifteen years to get the horse to the place he wanted. The next time it was faster because of the lessons he'd learned from the first horse. If you both enjoy your time spent together and you end up with a lovely horse at the end of it, what more can you ask for?

Training a horse can be a bit like property development. I was watching one of the various property programmes on TV one night and there was a couple who were renovating a house to sell on. They had done a nice job on the house but had started to go overboard and were buying things they didn't need, like installing an over the top £10,000 sound system into a basic two bed flat in Islington. They had got so far into the small details, they had completely forgotten about the bigger picture.

The presenter came to visit and after hearing about the expensive sound system, reminded them of the three most important things they should be focusing upon:

1. The price you buy the house at.

2. The price it costs to renovate the house.

3. The price you sell the house at.

I reckon it might be the same idea when training horses.

1. The initial price is the level of training you horse arrives when you buy him. This includes good training, bad training and any lack of training that exists.

2. Next is the amount and type of training you put into your horse.

3. The end result is when you add point 1 to point 2. This is your finished horse.

The Australian trainer mentioned that a friend of his walked 1,000k on foot with his horse to get his horse brave. That's quite impressive.

We chatted about horses a little longer while the high energy work was going on, and another interesting point was a question asked by an audience member.

'Is it ok to get off your horse if you are out on a hack and he doesn't want to pass something?'

The trainer nodded.

'I look at it this way. If you're going somewhere and horse refuses to go on, and you can see its going to escalate into the horse going backwards at speed down road and throwing all other horses in the ride into chaos, then there's nothing wrong with getting off your horse, leading him past and getting up again. It's safer than doing ninety miles an hour backwards down a road with cars coming towards you.'

Continuing on the traffic theme, the trainer added.

'There's another thing I see at clinics. If you ask your horse to stop then he should stop 'exactly' where you ask. Not kind of about here somewhere... Imagine there's a truck driving out right in front of you. If your horse doesn't stop, you'll get run over!'

Within about thirty minutes all the horses looked completely different and were chilled out and relaxed. Soon everyone was patting their horses all over with lots of energy. Once this was good it was followed by hopping up and down beside the horses and then jumping up bareback. There were smiles all round when they got up, as some of the horses were quite tall! That is actually one of the reasons I bought Ozzie – I've only got short legs so thankfully he's not that tall! You can do anything with a horse, as long as you get them ready.

They all moved on then to yields. A good few of the horses had their legs planted and didn't want to move them, so again it was noted that while those less experienced might live with their horses a bit stuck or braced or unwilling to move the way they want, a lot of the very good professionals just will not accept any sort of brace or leaning. If it is there, they start work at the very beginning of training to get rid of it. In this case, the little chestnut pushed forward when you asked it to move backwards, and the big bay didn't really want to move his front feet sideways. The big coloured horse definitely didn't like the sound of any of this and tried to kick the trainer as a sign of protest! How dare the trainer think he could be in charge of his feet!

Within about ten minutes a good start had been made by all horses and you could see their minds starting to change.

If you can move your horse's feet on demand any way you want – forwards, backwards, left, right – then this mentally is a huge thing for that horse. You are communicating to him in a nice and simple way that you are the one in charge of proceedings. Training a horse can be a bit like driving a car - the more you practise the better you get. The idea when your training your horse is that there shouldn't be a winner and a loser. Both of you should be winners.

With the more advanced people later on, it was straight into yields from a walk. So the horses would walk on a circle, then do a hindquarter yield, then immediately do a forequarter yield then walk on again. The idea was that it would be one smooth movement and you would have a nice rhythm through the whole movement. It was quite cool!

After this they walked with different types of walk, trot and canter. Can you ask your horse to walk slowly? Can you ask him to walk really slowly? How fast can he trot? Can he do a slow trot? How good are his transitions from walk to trot? Can you go from normal walk to fast trot? Can you go from fast walk to slow trot? So many ideas to bring home to Ozzie!

Towards the end of the session it got totally miserable and the rain started to pour down and there were reports that one car had got stuck in the car parking field.

Friday started off with another group chat. First up was to be aware when working with your horse to disassociate energy and emotion. Energy is a controllable action. Emotion is an uncontrolled action. So you might be able to walk, trot, canter, but can you halt exactly where you want, not just three steps later?

One lady had a question.

'But how do you stay emotionally detached? This is what I have problems with. When I watch you I see how grounded you always are, and you never get upset or let your emotions get to you. How can someone change how they react?

The trainer thought about it for a few seconds then replied quietly.

'To change something, you must first change yourself. Then everything else will change too.'

It did sound a bit abstract but it was true. You've got to come up with some kind of understanding inside yourself that changes how you view these situations. If you've got a thought process, you will have a different reaction. Humans think, then articulate the thought, then perform the associated action.

The idea is not to dominate your horse but to teach him instead. This trainer had a stallion who used to get worked up around mares. Instead of getting rough or over reacting, the trainer started to play with the boundaries. How close could he get to the other mares before the horse would start to get revved up? Then he stayed at this boundary, playing with it until the boundary started to move a little, until he could ride right up to the mares. It was an interesting way to approach it. You could do the same for herd bound horses.

Imagine Silver is in the corner of the arena. You want to ride around the arena on Tonto, but Tonto doesn't want to get too far from Silver. When Tonto thinks he has gone too far, he spins and bolts back to Silver. So how do you work on this?

Find out the exact limits of Tonto's movement before he panics spins and bolts back. Maybe he tosses head one second before he decides to bolt back. So when he tosses head, immediately turn him back nearer his friend, thus avoiding the bolt. Then continue playing like this. After while, the head toss will start to happen a little further away from Silver, until after a while if you use this system, you'll be able to walk Tonto all around the arena without him being worried about Silver at all. But you need to be able to read the signs and then react quickly.

There was another story about a horse who bolted out of creeks in Australia. As the horse headed towards creek, he would get tense. As the rider felt the horse start to tense up he was under orders to steer the horse away from the creek. After a while of doing this, the horse could get nearer and nearer to the creek without getting tense. The first time they did this, they had to work on this for about half a mile until the horse was calm enough to cross the creek nicely. By the end after another few sessions they could pretty much ride straight through it. When the owner got on, while she was told what to do, she couldn't feel the horse start to tense up. Instead the trainer walked in front of the horse and when he saw the horse start to tense up, yelled 'turn' to the rider. After a while of this the rider realised what was changing in the horse when he tensed up and soon enough she could do this on her own.

What I saw in each lesson is like what I do with Ozzie. You add in lots of small releases during the training sessions. Imagine a basket ball bouncing along. During each bounce the ball comes back down to the ground for an instant and then it goes off again. This is a bit like horse training. You do ask for things, but there are lots of little small releases every time you reward your horse, so there's not a build up of tension. Instead you get the opposite. Your horse relaxes on a regular basis and then can supple and lighten and get soft.

Ozzie was a bit like a big old parking area with lots of potholes. The potholes were of many different sizes, depths, and in different places all around the parking area. My job was to fill them in correctly. At the beginning I didn't know how many potholes there were. I focused on the potholes near to me first and started to fill them in. Then when they were done, I walked a few steps and noticed some more potholes. Then I filled those in too. How long it took to fill them in, and what kind of shovel, spade, machinery and equipment I used for each one was different depending on what type of pothole it was.

Ozzie and myself started off with a lot of potholes! It is quite nice though when you realise one day you've got a solid piece of ground to stand upon.

38. Ozzie says yes.

I arrived back to Dublin airport late on Sunday night after a mini scrum at the departure gates at Gatwick which I did not partake in. For some reason two flights had to leave at the same time through the same gates. I sat and chatted to my neighbour in the departures lounge (and I use that term loosely, a holding pen might be more accurate description) while the rest of the passengers battled it out. It is amazing how tiring sitting on a deckchair watching horses can be. I was out like a light once my head touched the pillow back in Clontarf.

Nine hours later I was woken by a text message from Marina wanting to know if we were still meeting at 1pm for the Dublin mini-marathon. During an unguarded moment a few months previously my arm had been twisted and I had signed up for just over six miles of agony around Dublin city centre. All that kept me going was the prospect of a pina colada afterwards. We had been doing a bit of training – jogging and gossiping after work – but my lack of any form of physical effect over the previous few days at the clinic in the UK was probably going to mean that I was not going to be at my peak performance level.

That afternoon I proceeded to jog like a lunatic around Dublin as innocent children waved us all on and local fireman hosed us down along the route. It was great fun and I even got a medal which I still cherish. We eventually retired to the pub at about 6pm, following closely by dinner in a Mexican restaurant in Georges St who had the most incredible chocolate cake with strawberry ice-cream.

Because of all my flying about I hadn't been home for about two weeks. In my absence Dad has been doing a little with Ozzie every few days, mainly walking and circling. Both were much improved now. After the clinic in England I had a few new things I wanted to do with Ozzie. First was getting him used to tolerating high energy which was never his strongest point.

So I drove down to Tipperary the following weekend, put on a halter and started with the rope and stick energy work. Ozzie was a bit nervy at the beginning so I decided it might be easier for him to follow me while I walked around the paddock doing this. We spent about an hour playing with this and he got much better.

He's not good with being patted either so later on I started off patting his back and hindquarters where he couldn't shy away too easily and then moved onto some shoulder patting.

Then we had some great fun with the leading at different gaits and doing different speeds in each. Oh my God did he match my every movement! Medium walk, fast walk, slow walk, stop, medium walk, fast walk, trot, canter. I walked slower, Ozzie saw this and then he also walked slower. I walked faster, he saw this and then he also walked faster. It was really good to see how much he was with me, mentally and physically. He just followed my speed and direction and enjoyed our mini blasts in canter about as I tried gainfully to stay with him! Two hours later I was about to pass out and Ozzie was still as cool as a cucumber, not even thirsty. Easily known which one of us was fit! I decided to quit on personal health grounds and came in for water.

One quick dog clipping later and it was back out for the bareback finale. We did a little loose rein leading at different gaits then patted Ozzie on his back (not a bother) lateral flexion and bounced about on either side. I got a leg up and lay over Ozzie with one leg on the near side and one leg along his back bone resting on his hindquarters. He wasn't bothered at all, just stood there on a loose rein. I got off, did this a few more times, and then went for gold... and sat up bareback!

The following Friday was the day Ireland said no to the Lisbon Treaty and Ozzie said yes to me. I put the tack on and started to throw stuff for fun right over his back to the ground on the far side. He didn't even blink. I got up then and rode around on a loose rein. I walked Ozzie in big circles for about half an hour. Every so often we did a direction change with some nice lateral flexion on rope cue then off we went again. It was all very basic stuff, but it was what he needed. Basic stuff done well, and done a lot. If I could continue like that, hopefully I'd see less of the big issues I had earlier that year. Dad also rode him for the first time. I had expected that Ozzie would kick at the change in weight on his back, but he tootled about like there was no difference.

At the end of the session, I spent about half an hour in the sun detangling his tail. It was all very zen. Ozzie did some tremendous awful stinky farts and a few leg muscle stretches from him too, where he bunched himself right up, gaining about two inches in height and lost a foot in length, then relaxed again. By the end he was half asleep with a droopy lower lip. When I was finished I took off his headcollar and walked back to the top of the paddock. He lifted up his head, thought for a moment and then started to walk up after me.

What a horse.

221

39. How do you catch a rabbit? You put salt on its tail.

Between the jigs and the reels, the awful weather that summer and my trips over to England, it was soon nearly the end of August.

'Empty contents of the sachet into a saucepan, gradually add 850mls (1 ½ pts) of cold water, stirring constantly.'

We had a barbecue happening on Saturday evening so I was on lunchtime cooking duty while Mum continued to make and bake for later on. I had only gone as far as 'empty contents of sachet into saucepan' when a sudden noise made me jump about three feet in the air.

'What are you doing!' My mother looked worriedly over at me as I held the soup packet over the pot. 'No, don't do it like that!'

I looked over at her and we both cracked up.

My mother is an excellent cook. She believes there are three ways to cook a meal.

1. Mum's method.
2. The method which is written on the back of the packet of food you are cooking.
3. Any other method.

Only one of these methods is correct. If you are cooking in the same house as Mum, then there is a special rule which states you must cook using Mum's method. At this stage as I dangled the packet of soup with a blank face, I decided to respectfully retire and offer my skills instead as a washer-upper and strawberry chopper. Thankfully this proceeded much more smoothly. I was not born a chef.

On Tuesday morning, still half asleep and on my way into work, I rang home to see how everyone was. They were all good. Dad had signed up for a kitesurfing lesson, Mum was heading off to Portugal for a week with a friend and my sister had managed to lock herself into the bathroom and had to be rescued by a neighbour down in Wexford.

Ozzie was also good. So good, that during the last two weeks no one could catch him. When I heard that I was itching to drive straight home to sort him out. Sadly I had to wait up in Dublin for the week (work as usual!) and it wasn't until that weekend that I could drive home and sort out my equine rebel.

I drove home on Thursday evening in good time and at about 8pm pulled up at the front of our horse. I hopped out of the jeep, saw Ozzie in the round pen and squished myself out through the fence and walked over to him. The gate to the round pen was open, but given the shortness of the grass in there it looked like he had been in there for most of the day.

'Hey Ozzie, how are you?' I rubbed his head and scratched his back. 'I hear you don't want to be caught, you daft idiot,' I continued, as I turned his head towards me on both sides. He gave me his best 'butter wouldn't melt' smile. He was a charming rogue.

I pretended I had a headcollar on him and led him with the imaginary lead rope over to the traditionally scary round pen gate and then out through it. He followed me quietly through it.

Then I walked the full length of the paddock up to the top to the water trough and he stayed right beside me the whole way in the invisible headcollar. I stopped beside the water and he dipped his head for a drink. Thinking that was a good start and getting hungry for my dinner, I started to walk away from him back to where I'd

223

abandoned my jeep. What did the twat do but look up and then start to follow me over to the jeep as well.

'Ozzie, I honestly don't know where I got you from.'

I parked my car, headed indoors, ate a quick spaghetti bolognaise and was introduced to Dad's new camera which had a very complicated specification sheet. Then it was back out to Ozzie with Dad. I caught him in the paddock and then put him in the round pen and took the halter off. Now it was time for Dad to catch him. While a horse is loose if you can rub them all over and stand at their shoulder and turn their head towards you, then you've pretty much got them caught. So that was the plan.

So I got Dad to rub Ozzie's back then shoulders. And rub properly — not pat-pat-pat but a good strong rub. It's good to concentrate on seeing if you can really rub all over your horse's face. When you really can rub all over his face with energy, then you can put one hand over the front of your horse's nose and pull it gently around to you. Once you've got the horse standing still with his nose to you it's an easy job to put the halter on.

Within about three minutes Dad had Ozzie caught on both sides and could rub all over his body and face with no headcollar on the horse.

It's funny how horses view people. Dougal views Dad as the boss. Even if I'm doing stuff with him, Dougal will do everything as asked but he's still aware of exactly where Dad is at all times and would do anything for Dad. If the two of us were in the field, he'd walk up to Dad first.

Ozzie is the opposite. He sees me as being his boss and I can do pretty much what I want with him. He doesn't have the same tolerance level with Dad, though once he's accepted that we are about, he will be pretty good for anyone. At one stage when Dad was trying to catch him, he wouldn't stand still. So I walked up to

224

Ozzie's back, stood by his side and rested my arm over his back where the saddle would go. He stood perfectly still ('oh no not Elaine again') and Dad walked straight up to his head and put on the halter straightaway and Oz didn't move a muscle.

****

'They were walking about Connemaras on the radio there Elaine,' Dad mentioned as I sat reading the papers.

'Connemaras'? I replied as my ears pricked up.

'Yeah I think someone was on Pat Kenny... they reckoned they were fairly tough and hardy, and they need a fair bit of work.'

I nodded my head in agreement. 'Sounds about right.'

On Friday morning, I woke up at 9am and at 9.30am spent the next hour and a half doing Ozzie. There was a guy up chain-sawing timber at the top of the paddock, so it was good to get Ozzie to ignore him and just focus on the work I wanted him to do. I did some one line work with him and after a bit of messing in the canter, did some really nice walk and trot transitions. No arguments, no fuss, just really nice and easy. That was good. I did about five minutes of hindquarter and forequarter yields, sidepassing, and rubbing his head all over with the rope. Then I brought him back up near the chainsaw man, dropped the lead rope and left him stand there, and threw on all the tack – saddle, bridle, headcollar and longlines. It was the first time I had used longlines on him. He just zoned out and relaxed. I put the bit in and out a few times and he was grand with it, so then I put it in again and did up the bridle. Again no issues.

I longlined him around the paddock and did various figures of eights and circles and a few backups. Then Dad appeared back up on the quad so we did a bit of a demo for him too. It was all pretty nice work. Ozzie was a little nervy when the longlines touched his

225

near hindquarters but he got over it. Then I took off the longlines and just did some more one rein work on the circle with the bridle in. I got some more really nice and soft walk and trot transitions so I was quite chuffed. He did tend to get a bit revved up and kind of bounced into the trot so it was nice to see him changing gait but keeping the softness and rhythm. Dad did a little as well as I was going back to Dublin for four weeks and he was going to do some work with Ozzie in my absence. As he longlined him about he remarked:

'He is incredibly light on the longlines Elaine. The only weight I have in my hands is of the longlines themselves.'

He did some nice halt and backups with Ozzie as well. All that early rope work we did the previous year was really standing to Ozzie. It was also the first time I had seen Ozzie really concentrate on what he was doing. He had this amazing work ethic going on and had complete focus on what he was being asked to do. He was totally committed to the job and all his attention was on what I was asking him to do.

'Yeah. It's quite nice to have a horse who doesn't lean on the bit at all isn't it?'

Oz smiled to himself. He had known he was brilliant all along. It had just taken us humans a while to figure it out.

****

'I tell you, in this country you wouldn't want to go planning a barbecue'.

Mum was lamenting the weather. It wasn't looking good. I was on window cleaning and yard sweeping duties to help tidy the place up for that evening's festivities. Ozzie was enjoying himself eating grass with no one putting weird bits or ropes around him. The plan for the BBQ currently was for Dad to barbecue in the rain,

226

sheltered by a gazebo which would definitely not blow away. Everyone else would shelter indoors and admire Ozzie out the window (though I'm not sure if that last bit was in the official plan.)

On Saturday morning I caught Ozzie, put on his tack and clipped the longlines onto the bit. He was lovely – very sensitive to the reins and from very small cues on the reins, turned, went forward, stopped and backed up. He also did some more nice 'walk to trot to walk' transitions on the one line afterwards, including only turning to me when asked. Other than that he would follow my speed exactly and stop beside me if I stopped, still facing the way he had been moving. He really was concentrating on me. He was caught again a few times in the round pen. When I took the bit out, I noticed he had somehow managed to chew half way through the straight happy mouth which I had been using for him. He was some horse. I had a Rockin S French link as well I bought a while back with him in mind, so I popped that in afterwards and it seemed ok. It's nicer than a normal french link bit as it doesn't pinch the corners of the mouth and its quite stable.

As we had twelve people coming over later, it was back into the yard and a quick clean up so Ozzie was looking his best. I sorted out his mane and tail while he ate the bushes. It might be raining that evening but at least Ozzie would look well. I put him back out again, and then for fun brought out the yard brush and a big brown paper bag to show him. Soon both were under assault.

****

'I never had much luck with greys.'

The BBQ had gone exceedingly well and I was in the middle of a post dinner horse conversation with one of our neighbours.

'It was a few years ago, but we'd bought this grey. I thought he could make a nice one day eventer for the kids.'

227

I nodded my head.

'My brother had picked him out, and he'd be fairly good at judging horses.'

'How did you get on with him' I asked.

She shook her head. 'We didn't really. He was very nappy. He wouldn't go into a stable, and he wouldn't go out of a stable. He used buck people off every while as well. In the end we sold him on at the sales.'

'Oh no' I replied, 'that's a pity. I bought Ozzie last year so he was pretty green too.'

'Oh? He's nappy too?' she enquired looking at me with interest.

'No,' I smiled, 'but we couldn't touch him anywhere. I'd seen him with tack on when I bought him, but if I'd tried to ride him when we got home I would have been bucked from here to Kilfeacle. It would have blown his mind.'

Her brow deepened with interest and she looked across at me. 'Right. Well listen, if you're looking for someone to proof read your book, I'd be more than delighted, just let me know.'

I smiled. 'Thanks, you're very kind. I might do actually. I should have a new version ready in a few weeks... would that be ok?

'Yes. I'll look forward to it!'

****

On Sunday we repeated all of the weekends work. We did more one rein transitions, longlining off the rockin s bit, catching with Dad and walking about in hand. What was unusual was that during each session Ozzie was consistently perfect. This was not normal! Usually we would get a bit of nice then a bit of 'nah' then some

228

more nice stuff. I wasn't going to say anything then as if I did it might have tempted fate, but let's just say I was starting to feel a bit more optimistic. I realised that the way to Ozzie's heart was through patience, persistence, fun and lots of work. Perhaps we were getting closer to our goal.

40. Don't put an air freshner in the fridge

It had been just under four weeks since I had been home so I took Friday off work and on Thursday night I hit the road to Tipperary. It had rained in Ireland for the previous two weeks but there was glorious weather in Tipperary all weekend. I woke up early on Friday and suddenly found myself part of a doubles tennis match in Tipperary town, so that was good fun. I drove back home afterwards and one quick orange juice and biscuit later I hopped out to do the horse. I had a huge list of tasks I wanted to get done with him. He saw me approach and started to walk towards me. Now when I say walk I actually mean hobble... the poor horse was lame in his near fore. It was a bit like the man flu. Probably not that bad but required a lot of sympathy.

Anyway, I gave him a rub and tried to figure out what to do. It was such a lovely day it would have been a pity if I couldn't spend a bit of time with him. 'Bingo' I thought. I would pull his mane!

Poor Ozzie spent the next two hours standing still loose in his paddock as I valiantly pulled and tugged at his mane. He amused himself by eating the plastic curry comb and kicking around a box of strawberries I had earmarked for the horses. Cute enough he wouldn't eat them. Oh no. He just wanted to play football with the box. Anyway, it was nice to spend a bit of time with him. Sometimes I did wonder about him though. After two hours of mane pulling, I left him and walked back up to the top of the paddock, and he made it his business to limp up after me staying right beside me the whole way. Dad saw him as well and started to call him 'Dinny' after a similar guy who used to walk with a limp on Glenroe, an Irish TV soap.

The next day it was up again and out to the tennis courts for a two against one match, which we barely won. I'd come up with a few things to do with a horse who could only stand still, so I headed out again after lunch with some brushes, a red rug, a stick and string, a plastic bag and a polocrosse stick and ball. Ozzie hobbled up to me again when he saw me coming. I gave him a bit of sympathy and scratches again so he was alright.

Then I spent about two hours mucking about as he stood still half asleep in the sunshine beside me. He got his tail brushed, the red rug was throw on from every direction, I waved the stick like a mad woman while walking the full way around him, rubbed him with the plastic bag, and then put the plastic bag on the end of the stick and went a bit mad with that as well while I walked around him again. He was very chilled out. In fact he was nearly asleep for most of it.

I had the polocrosse stick and ball out, so under the watchful eye of our dog, I kicked it all around Ozzie's feet, dribbled the ball along his back, made it fall off his back and hindquarters and then threw the ball completely over his back. He was not at all bothered. Then I got the stick, waved it about a bit and rubbed him with it. I needed a bit of work myself so then I started to throw the ball high into the air and caught it with the net all around Ozzie. He was as cool as a cucumber. I put him out into the bigger paddock with Dougal at the end, and he still insisted in walking along beside me as I messed around doing some polocrosse ball work as I walked with him. We headed up to Dougal. They were delighted to see each other and soon departed off for some grass. There wasn't really much more I could have done with him anyway.

On Sunday morning, rain had just cleared so I was just going to do some accounts, have lunch and then head back up to Dublin. I had a quick look out to the two horses and saw Ozzie lying down halfway up the paddock with Dougal standing guard. I couldn't resist, so I put on some boots and walked up to them. I did about ten years of pony club as a youngster, so safety was important and one thing we were always told was don't sit down beside a horse. You might not be able to get out of the way quick enough if something happens. Which is dead right. But anyway I reckoned it

231

was too nice not too, so I sat down beside Ozzie and leaned back against him, and we both enjoyed the morning sun as my jeans got wet from the dew on the grass. It was worth it. I was quite fond of my little horse.

Later that evening I arrived back up to Dublin. I lived with three others, a Spanish girl, a Swedish girl and an Irish guy who was addicted to football. He had a few funny ideas which didn't always work. He also had an issue throwing out things. Our fridge was one example. It was full to the brim of half consumed tubs and bottles of God knows what. From time to time I dumped all the out of date stuff out of it. That evening there was a funny smell coming out of the fridge when I opened it. As my eyes moved over the tubs of out of date butter and ham, they stopped abruptly on a white plastic object. He had put an air freshener in the fridge. I nearly fell over, told the others and then we all cracked up. You couldn't make this stuff up.

41. Confidence and slugs

I am not really that squeamish at all unless you're talking about snakes or big spiders or things that jump from one side of the room to the other at speed. If you asked me what I thought about slugs, I really couldn't give you much of an opinion. I don't usually meet many of them. But I've met a few of the buggers recently and I tell you I don't bloody like them.

I was still living in the house where the solution to life's problems was an air freshener. I had noticed a bit of rising damp on one of the walls in my bedroom as well but I had made an executive decision to ignore it. Then one evening I was reading a book and I head this very quiet ''sssshhh' sound. It was a bit weird because it would repeat itself quietly about every two or three seconds. I couldn't figure out what the hell it was. Anyway, I donned some protective equipment (pyjamas and goldy-brown flip flops) and set about snooping around my room following the noise. It didn't seem to be coming from the chimney so as my eyes glazed over the floor boards in front of me I was met with the sight of the biggest fattest most ignorant slug I had ever met, so fat and bloated that I could hear him breathing. Or squelching along. Or whatever it was doing that was making that awful sound. Anyway I put my brave face on, wrinkled my nose, scooped it up onto a book and threw it out the window. It was rotten but I was a grown up so I could deal with it. It was a one off right?

Fast forward to about three weeks later. I arrived back up to Dublin on Saturday night. Later that night I was in bed and as I checked a text on my phone the light of the screen shone up against the wall beside my head. I saw a black stripe up there which wasn't usually there. 'No way' I thought, half asleep. On went the PPE again and I turned on the light and approached the bed. Oh no. For all that was sweet and holy. It was another bloody slug. It wasn't quite as fat so if it was the first one making a re-appearance at least he had gone on a diet since I'd last seen him. I freaked out and then threw the bugger out the window again. That was it. I needed to move houses. I couldn't deal with any more midnight slugs.

Aside from the slug attack I did actually have quite an enjoyable weekend. My brother's friend had an ex-racehorse she wanted to do a bit of riding with so on Saturday morning I headed down to Wexford to meet both of them and see how they were getting on.

The forecast was for rain, but it held off and soon I was sailing down the N11 happy as Larry unaware of the slug issue I would have later than night. Soon I pulled up outside a nice house on the outskirts of Wexford.

I pulled on all my winter gear and knocked on the front door. My trusty wax jacket was at least fifteen years old and looked it was in better shape than ever.

The door opened and a friendly face peered out.

Hiya, you must be Elaine!' The Wexford accent is very cool.

'Hello Pia, yes I am! How are you?'

We headed out soon after and found a lovely big thoroughbred eating grass up in one of the fields. As we walked up I asked her where she wanted to start with him.

'Well, Row was doing some point to points, but the trainer said at the start of the summer that his heart wasn't in them anymore. I didn't really mean to get a horse but he just came along, so I'd like to do a bit of work with him and maybe then just do some local events. There're gallops on the beach nearby, and maybe I could do some cross county or hunting with him. Just fun stuff really.'

It sounded like a good plan alright.

'So do you know the last time he was ridden?' I asked her.

234

'Well, it was before the summer anyway. I have sat up on him once or twice, but to be honest I didn't know how he was going to react so I didn't really do much with him. He's been out all summer and I've just spent time with him but haven't really done anything. He's just got new shoes on this week. Basically I guess I'd like to start at the beginning and build up a relationship and get to know him. I guess when you get a bit older you confidence goes a bit, so I'd just like to build our confidence.'

I nodded my head.

'That sounds good alright. What we might do, if you think it sounds ok, is bring him into a small paddock and just run through all the basics and see how far we get. If he can do everything perfectly we'll get onto the more complicated things. How would that sound?'

I looked over at her enquiringly.

'Grand' she smiled back. We arrived over to Row and he was nice and sociable and stood happily while I caught him. Pia led him down to the yard. I held him while she went off to lock up the dogs, and I backed him up a step every time he decided he wanted to move off somewhere. He was really gorgeous!! Very light to move and very sensitive.

Pia came back over a few minute later. 'It's probably a bit early to say this but I think you've got a cracker of a horse here.

Pia smiled. 'Ah thanks. He is a gentleman. He was looking after the youngsters in his paddock all summer.'

I gave him back to Pia and we headed into the small paddock and she walked Row around the perimeter once or twice.

'Right', I said, 'if you can come into the centre that'd be great. I might borrow him for a second if that's alright.'

His leading was pretty good, so I spent a minute or two polishing it up a little. One thing I noticed straight away was that while he was doing as I asked he spent a fair bit of time with his head looking into the distance and with his mind outside the paddock as opposed to in it with the two of us.

I got Pia to do this as well so it all went fine. Next up was desensitisation. The plan was to rub him all over with a hand, then pat him all over, then use a numnah and the stick and run them all over him too. It was basically to see was he confident with things happening in close proximity to him. He was ok-ish with being rubbed but wasn't completely sure about standing still when the patting and the numnah throwing started. We did a bit and played around with his tolerance level. He was more spooky on his far side. I guess it was a bit like getting a structural engineer out to have a look at a house. We were trying to figure out what type of a horse we had on our hands and see what issues he had, and then we could come up with a list of things to concentrate on. Desensitising would be one of them anyway.

He was pretty light on his feet so we did some suppling work next. We turned the neck while his feet stayed still (better on the near side), and then moved the front legs on their own, then the back legs on their own, and did some backing up. He really was lovely with all of these. The one issue he had during the backing up, was on the far side he wasn't completely comfortable standing still with his neck turned, or with someone patting his back on the far side. The hindquarter yield itself was no problem. Pia did all of these as well really nicely and without taking any backward steps herself. But again we were returning to the confidence issue.

Because of this, I thought it might be useful to show Pia some high energy work. I suspected Row would not be too comfortable with it, but if she wanted to go out riding him she'd be much safer if he could tolerate a bit of energy in his environment – like kids running across a road, a dog barking, bicycle coming up behind him, a horse getting unruly near him or whatever.

'Pia. What I'd like to do as well is for you to hold Row on a loose rein and I am going to go to the far side of the paddock and just wave this stick around a bit to see how much Row can tolerate.'

Row was currently standing quietly, relaxed and chilled out and still interested in what was going on outside the arena, but not as much as he had been.

'Grand Elaine, go for it.'

So off I headed, and when I was as far away as I could get, I turned around and started to gently wave the long stick and rope from side to side. That got his attention straight away. He looked a bit nervous and took a step or two. When he stood still I stopped waving the stick. We did this a few times and his tolerance for the energy I was creating was really pretty low. I put the stick down and walked back up to Pia and Row and gave him a rub. He relaxed again.

'There is definitely some confidence work there you could be doing with him I reckon.'

Pia nodded her head.

'Basically he is very well behaved, lovely and light and supple and his brakes are great. His mind wanders away though and he gets worried and panics a little at small stuff. Particularly on the off side. That probably would come through into his riding as well.'

I thought for a minute.

'I might just try one more thing,' I said, 'if you don't mind'.

'No, fire ahead,' she said.

'I just want to see if Row can follow a feel. Basically if he feels the lead rope moving right very gently, will he move right too? And same for the left. Just to see how his steering is.'

'Grand, go for it.'

I had the long stick in my other hand, but wasn't using it. I stood in front of the horse. The horse had positioned himself so I was in his near eye. I raised up my left hand to ask him to do a anti-clockwise circle in walk. His body was already pointed this way so I reckoned it'd be an easy place to start. He was very responsive and moved into a walk without an issue. His near eye was on the inside.

I asked him to stop and he did a nice hindquarter yield and turned in. Next up I pointed out with my right hand, to ask him to do a clockwise circle. He started to keep going the way he had been (anti-clockwise). I started to bump the lead rope and he started to get worried and go faster in an anti-clockwise direction. I stopped him and had a think. We had a little issue here. He didn't want to move clockwise around me. As he stood looking at me I noticed he had positioned himself again so that I was in his near eye.

'Right,' I said. 'I think Row feels a lot more confident when he can see me out of his near eye. So you see every time I ask him to stop he positions himself to my left so I'm on his near side, and when I asked him to circle clockwise so I would be on his off side, he got a bit panicky.'

'Yeah, I do,' Pia replied.

'This is probably the same as the rubbing and patting earlier on when he was more nervous on his off side as well. I'll just see if I can get around it.'

I stood in front of the horse, and this time held the stick up along but not touching his off side. He stood there but looked at me quizzically. Then with my right hand I pointed out to the right with the lead rope. If he went anticlockwise he'd walk straight into the stationary stick (which he didn't really like). The other option would be to do as I asked and walk in a clockwise circle with me in his far eye. I asked him very lightly again and he took off at a light

238

trot the way I had asked, so I was in his far eye. I asked him for a hindquarter yield and brought him back to a halt. Again he stood so I was back in his near eye.

'He's got you back in his near eye again Elaine,' Pia said.

'Yep,' I replied. 'He's really not 100% on the off side is he?'

Pia shook her head. 'No, he's not.'

So again I stood in front of him, put my stick on his far side, and very gently cued him to walk on clockwise around me. This time he didn't trot and just stepped sideways and then walked around.

'Good,' I remarked, 'that's better.' I did this a few more times. When I wanted him to go anticlockwise it was very easy I didn't need to use the stuck as a pretend wall. When I wanted him to go clockwise I would always put the stick near his far side, before I asked him to walk on.

I explained what I was doing to Pia and then she spent a while doing this as well. She was quite chuffed when she got a few nice hindquarter yields from a distance. Row did really well, and soon was walking on both reins and stopping lightly with no fuss. But Pia always had the stick in place before she asked him to put her in his far eye.

I had brought out the saddle as well but I reckoned at this stage we'd done enough for one day. We took him back into the yard, gave him a rub and left him go. He was a cool horse – social, well behaved and friendly. He just lacked a bit of confidence and was a bit nervy on his off side. We headed into the house for a Danish pastry.

'You've got a lovely horse there Pia,' I said as I wrote down about twenty items of homework on the back of a large postcard.

'He's happy around people and he's sensitive and clever. He's got great manners and he can do all the lateral stuff in his sleep. Where he falls down is his confidence in what's happening near him, particularly when it's in his off eye. I reckon it's something worth doing a bit of work on. He's got lots of potential though. You've got a nice horse on your hands.'

Pia nodded. 'Yes I agree.' She looked down at the never ending list of homework I was still writing. 'I think I'll be busy anyway! I'll focus on that confidence stuff as I can see the difference in him on both sides alright. It'd be good to do this stuff though and spend time and get to know him more as well. Other than that I was just going to lunge him but it probably wouldn't teach him much really.'

'He'd get pretty fit though,' I replied with a smile.

'Great,' she said throwing her eyes up to heaven. He had actually won his first race out as a young horse so he probably had no shortage of speed in him.

'Best of luck with him anyway, let me know how you get on. You have my email anyway.'

'I will do,' Pia replied. 'Thanks very much for coming down.'

'No worries,' I replied back with a grin.

****

It's useful to realise that horse like us can have confidence issues too. The next day I met another horse with a similar issue.

****

The next horse had been on box rest for a good while and for the last year or so had been out in the field. She was very attached to another horse, to the extent that she would always stand right beside him no matter where he was.

240

We caught her and led her down to the arena as the rest of the horses followed us down to. She was lovely actually. She had a gentle nature and she really wanted to please. She could handle being rubbed and patted all over and she had some lovely lateral work and was quite soft and very responsive. But she had very little confidence in herself. Her attention was leaving the arena quite often, as she peered out to where the other horses were.

When I brought out the stick and stood half an arena away from her and waved it about with a bit of energy, she really couldn't stand it. We played around a bit, so her tolerance of things was noticeably higher when her owner stood right beside her. But when she was on her own she got worried much faster. You could see how this would impact her herd boundness when she was out in the field as well. She just really wasn't confident dealing with things on her own. We worked a little on this and after about twenty minutes she was standing on her own and her tolerance for the scary girl with the mad stick had got quite a lot better and she was now more comfortable with us and wasn't leaving the arena mentally as often as she had been.

She hadn't really been ridden I'd say in over a year and before that she had been injured so I would have guessed as she was she would have had issues hacking out on her own. She was cool though – she really wanted to do the right thing for us and you could nearly see her brain ticking over trying to work things out. She was one of those horses who was happier standing politely glued to your side, rather than doing her own thing. But you could definitely work on improving this stuff, as even that twenty minutes had shown. I left them with more homework to do. It really does often come back to confidence as a starting point.

That Monday the farrier came out to our house in Tipperary to do the two horses. When I rang home that evening Joseph had got a drop out of Ozzie's front foot and Dougal was now sound again. Both horses had got fresh grass in their paddock and had spent a while that evening galloping around it delighted with themselves.

241

It's nice to visit people and work with other horses but I have to say I enjoy working with Ozzie the most.

I was looking forward to my next trip home.

42. Everything comes together.

It was early October and as I headed down to Tipperary the radio was full of talk about the recession, house prices drops and the stock markets falling. It seemed the government in their wisdom had decided a good idea would be to take away most of the over 70's medical cards and increase school class sizes. There was literally a mutiny in the country as half of it saw red. The banks had a bit of a wobble one day as well after a radio talk show pointed out that only savings in the post office were guaranteed, so then the other half of the country quickly withdrew their company from the main banks, prompting the bank leaders to go cap in hand to the government to beg for a state guarantee on all deposits. Builders were going bust as no one was buying overpriced houses anymore. A lot of people were getting caught in negative equity. There were certainly going to be interesting times ahead.

While Ozzie hadn't done anything over the past two weeks, I was pretty motivated that this weekend we would fly through the groundwork, have no issues and soon be riding around. It had been about a month since we'd done any 'just do as I ask and don't argue' work together, so if I hadn't had been as enthusiastic perhaps I would have twigged that this lack of recent leadership work, coupled with a lack of any work during the last two weeks might mean Ozzie might not be as keen as I was to go riding.

I brought out the saddle and bridle and left it on the fence. Then I caught Ozzie, popped on a halter and twelve foot rope and asked him to walk, trot and canter around me. Mum was out gardening in our front garden at the time.

Walk was fine.

Trot was fine.

243

By canter Ozzie had had enough and proceed to alternative between stopping dead, galloping like an idiot, cow kicking in towards me and reversing and going up on his two hinds legs. I asked him to stop and then led him over to the post and rail fencing where I put on my hat and clipped on a longer line.

Mum has walked over to the fence at this stage.

'What's he doing all that stuff for? I don't like that now at all!'

I have to admit I didn't like it myself much either.

She looked over, worried, at the saddle, which was still sitting on the fence.

'You're not thinking of riding him today are you?'

I could have gone through Ozzie for a shortcut. I'd done all the work with him. I knew he could be ridden. We'd been through all the leadership / argument stuff already and I really had hoped we'd gone past it.

I shook my head. 'Nope, it doesn't look like I'll be riding today. '

I took Ozzie out again on a longer rope, and soon he obediently walked, trotted and cantered around on both reins with no fuss.

On Sunday I repeated the same thing again, so he was much improved. No arguments at all.

When I thought about it, I reckoned that Ozzie needed consistent work. The most I could get home was about every second weekend, so things were quite stop-start-ish, which wasn't helping matters. I wasn't too sure of a way out of it. I'd have to think about what I was going to do.

Thankfully I wasn't the only one thinking about what was to be done. I suspect Mum told Dad of what she had seen of Ozzie's antics, so about a week later I got a text message from Dad to say that he was doing a little work with Ozzie each day. Walk, trot, canter on the lunge, saddle and bridle on, leaning over Ozzie's back, longlining, leading around and handling. So I was quite looking forward to our next session in Tipperary.

I drove down to Tipperary on Saturday morning to avoid the traffic, and the weather once again was horrendous. Rain, rain and more rain.

During lunch Dad was quite keen to get out and do Ozzie asap, so that afternoon we managed to do about ten minutes of walk – trot – canter a long line in between showers of rain. It was actually pretty good going given the weather.

On Sunday, I'd say probably Ozzie's tenth day of continuous work of some sort, I headed out early and did some groundwork with him, where I controlled the speed and direction of each one of his four legs. We did yields, sidepassing, turns, various speeds and backups. He just simply did everything I asked without a bother.

I left him go and came in for coffee. After coffee Dad and I went out. Dad brought a tacked up Ozzie out to the big field, and did a quick walk, trot and canter on both reins. No issues. Then I brought him in, tacked him up and then out appeared Dad in a riding hat.

Ozzie stood like a rock as Dad got on. Ozzie looked a little bit worried so the three of us stood there. After a minute or two Ozzie's body relaxed and the head came down.

Then Dad started to walk Ozzie about in various directions. By the end of forty-five minutes Ozzie was walking and trotting around nicely, looking pretty relaxed and chilled with no issues at all. What a cool little horse.

Monday morning was beautiful – a blue sky and the sun was shining. While Dad was down the farm I threw on the tack, brought him out to the field and did walk, trot and canter on the longline and then brought him into the round pen as Dad drove up on the quad. I did a few more things and Dad dropped the quad back to the stables and returned out again, hat in hand.

I also had my hat in my hand.

'Right, I'm riding him today.'

'Grand' said Dad. 'I might as well too.' The poor horse. He seemed to have gone from one part-time trainer to two full time riders.

I mounted from the far side and again Ozzie stood like a rock. When I sat up there, there was no worry on Ozzie's part. He was totally relaxed. I walked him around and soon the two of us were trotting around on both reins like we'd been doing it for years. He was such a lovely horse to ride. Comfortable, a nice long stride, very light on the reins, easy to turn, perfect brakes, good impulsion, and very quick to respond to all cues. He was just amazing. He was even more solid than on Sunday. He didn't ride like a green horse.

When I stopped, quick as a flash Dad had his hat on, so he hopped up and trotted Ozzie around again both ways. Ozzie didn't put a foot out of place. It was nice to have a horse who didn't mind different riders. Then on I hopped again and did the same thing. Ten minutes later once I stopped to give Ozzie a mental rest and dismounted, Dad put his hat on again and rode around.

Ozzie was just solid. I don't know any other way to describe it. Mentally he was totally with us. Emotionally he was balanced and confident. Physically he was soft and relaxed, chilled out and did everything we asked him to do straight away.

246

'So what do you think of him' I asked Dad from my position up in the saddle. Dad looked up at me.

'I'll tell you what I like about him Elaine. I love the reins. There's no weight in them at all.'

One thing Dad used to say about my grandfather was that he believed it was possible to train a horse so he could be ridden using two pieces of thread.

'What else I like is that he's so good when you're getting up and down. And I love how easy he is to turn, go and stop.'

I smiled and gave Ozzie a rub.

'I hope your proud of yourself mister. You are a pretty cool horse.'

Ozzie sighed in reply.

For Ozzie the best way forward was to keep him busy with some regular handling or riding each day to keep building on what we had achieved.

One week later, Ozzie and I were cantering happily all around the paddock. He was perfect in pretty much every way. There were no more arguments. The gait changes up and down were pushbutton and the brakes were spot on. I could turn him from my seat, he had softness through his body and I had no weight in my hands. Most important of all, Ozzie was happy and confident as we rode around together.

I realised then that we had both learned a lot over the previous year.

I had definitely bought the right horse.